His Appointed Times

Hebrew / Gregorian Calendar
Journal & Study Guide

Discover The Lord's Prophetic Calendar
In Real-Time In Your Life

December 2020 thru January 2022

Christine Vales

Published in St Simons Island, GA by Christine Vales.

Printed in the United States of America.

ISBN-13: 9798657293197

Scripture quotations are from the New American Standard (NASB) version of the Bible.
Copyright © 1960, 1962, 1963, 1968, 1971, 1972, 1973, 1975, 1977, 1995, by The Lockman Foundation.

Original Covers & Artwork by Christine Vales, Copyright © 2020.

Dedication

To you, the reader.

May you receive encouragement and confirmation in your steps
as you use this prophetic resource in your walk with Jesus.
May it lead you to a fresh revelation of His great love
for you with every sunrise and sunset.
Psalm 108:4

Blessings in Yeshua,
Christine

Acknowledgements

I have been so blessed to be surrounded by
a circle of such encouraging hearts during this work.
Thank you Mom, Trish, Jennifer, Sandi, Debby, Kelly, Danielle and Bill.
I am blessed to be loved and spurred on by each of you!

—

To my beloved, Carlos.
My heart is full of joy when I think of the endless encouragement,
wisdom, laughter and love we have shared together
as I fulfill the ministry He has graciously given me.
I love you!
xox

Thank You, Lord

...for your great love for me that gives me boldness, confidence
and joy that spurs me on to good works... even creating
this fifth edition of "His Appointed Times."

"Faith worketh by love."
Galatians 5:6

"And these are they which are sown on good ground. Such as hear the word and receive it and bring forth fruit. Some thirtyfold, some sixty and some a hundred."
Mark 4:20

This Book Belongs To:

_____

Name

_____

Date

Words of Testimony

"The Hebrew calendar is not a new idea. It was instituted by God to keep His children in His perfect time. I've been studying the Hebrew calendar with Christine for years and can testify God's divine calendar never disappoints. His mercy is new every morning and every season continues to come alive with renewed hope. Christine's heart for the Lord and gift of encouragement that she uses in creative and refreshing ways keeps pointing us to look to Jesus in her 'His Appointed Times' teachings. Now more than ever we need to be reminded God never changes and His goodness can be found each and every day no matter what is going on in the world."

Trish Hall
Delighted In Jesus
www.delightedinjesus.com

"This calendar is exactly what I have been searching for. Finding and meeting Christine and this wonderful book of insight has been enriching, empowering and fulfilling. Christine is a soul sister and we are from the same tribe. The appointed times calendar and journal provides incredible insight for the body of Christ. It helps us understand and incorporate the whole counsel of God. What some consider intimidating or hidden secrets come alive and become applicable. The beauty, creativity, explanations and teachings Christine has laid out bridge us to the roots of our faith and propel us into our prophetic destiny. This is a must have resource for your spiritual arsenal."

Pastor Jennifer Mallan
Pastor - Reliant Family Church, Tampa, FL
www.reliantfamilychurch.com

"'Breathe Again!' This is God breathing into every fiber of our being through His calendar by Christine Vales. It is God's pure oxygen from the beginning of time, long before the troubles of this world knocked the breath out of many of us. Life will not knock the breath out of us anymore. Put on His Word and enjoy breathing fresh air again as He lives His life through us. He is making things beautiful in His time on His calendar."

Bill Yount
Blowing the Shofar Ministries
www.billyount.com

"Christine's passion to awaken us to God's appointed calendar has become contagious! The women of our church eagerly await each month's chalkboard teaching to discern how to align to 'His Appointed Times' to fully receive all that God has for us. Her calendar has so enriched our spiritual journey as we have watched His hand confirm over and over again that seasons and times matter. May your journey with Christine stir your faith, awaken your spirit and recalibrate your life to live in sync with His plans and purposes for His Beloved. What a gift this book is for those of us who seek to truly know Him more!"

Rochelle Frazier
Author - Pastor - Counselor
www.rochellefrazier.com   www.ninetyoneabbeylane.com

"'Ahhhhhhhhhhhhhhhh'... This is my expression of pure satisfaction regarding the content of Christine Vales' 'His Appointed Times' calendar, journal and study guide. As I look for the Lord bringing together His 'one new man,' Jew and Gentile, I am convinced that books such as this will inspire that merger, like nothing else. Christine's ability to blend her easily understood monthly renderings with the depth of Biblical Hebrew insights makes otherwise confusing concepts understandable, and fun. You will see (and want to share) scripture in a whole new way."

Caz Taylor
Prophetic Teacher & Author - Salem Media Group, San Diego broadcaster
www.facebook.com/CazTaylor

"We have been grafted into a rich heritage through Abraham, Isaac and Jacob paid for by the blood Jesus and it's our legal right to tap into all the benefits it has for us. In 'His Appointed Times' Christine Vales has created an amazing way for us to connect with God and stay in His timing and know how He is moving in the earth. As one who studies God's prophetic calendar, Christine's book has become a valuable resource for me. She truly has created a treasure."

Susan Cheatham
Susan Cheatham Ministries
www.scmfire.org

Table of Contents

Introduction

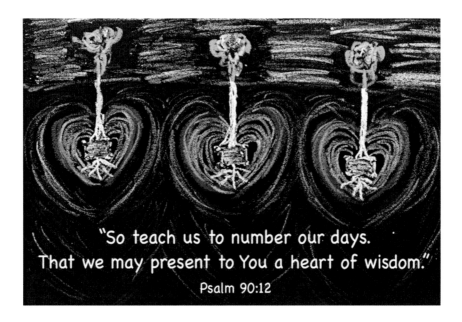

"So teach us to number our days.
That we may present to You a heart of wisdom."

Psalm 90:12

It's Time to Get Back in Time With Him

The Lord established a calendar. His calendar. The Hebrew calendar.
He has not changed it or gotten off of it. We have.

We have been trained to believe the Gregorian calendar is *the* authority of time as we know it.
We are called to live and operate *in* this world, however, we are called not to be *of* it.
We are instructed to walk in His ways and this includes how the Lord keeps time.

So...what do think of when you think of time?
Most of us think of time with a negative connotation.

Thoughts like...
"I am running out of time"   "My best days are behind me"   "I am running late"
"I am too old"   "I missed my window of opportunity" or "I'll never finish this"

All these negative thoughts are exactly what the enemy wants us to believe.
In fact, the devil wants to deceive us with a lot more than just a piece of fruit.

Check out this scripture that gives us insight on the enemy's plan to change times, seasons and laws...
*"He (Satan) will speak out against the Most High and **wear down the saints of the Highest One,**
and he will intend to **make alterations in times and in law.** (Dan 7:25)*

Are you feeling worn down lately?
It probably has to do with how you are observing time.
However, now you know who has been behind it.

Don't lose heart! Be encouraged!
The Lord is outside of time, yet He made time for us and for His purposes.

Hidden like a treasure beneath the surface of our modern-day Gregorian calendar,
lies a timepiece of the Ancient of Days. Time is good because He created it.
He separated the light from the darkness and created days, weeks, months and years.
In addition, He set appointed times for His people to meet with Him. He did all of this for us.
He set up divine appointments on His calendar to help us stay in fellowship with Him and not drift.
He wanted us to be encouraged and to always have something to look forward to on the calendar.
He established His weekly, monthly and annual cycles to help us grow and abide in Him and His ways.

The enemy wants to get us out of sync with the Lord's timing. However, in these days,
the Lord is restoring all things to His people including His prophetic timepiece. (Acts 3:20-21)

Be encouraged as you go through the pages of this book.
May you receive revelation knowledge of the great unconditional love of the Father,
who created you and time itself. Truly our times are in His hands. (Ps 31:15)

Have fun getting back in time with HIM!

Shalom in Yeshua (Jesus),
Christine

Where Did This Idea Come From?

For the past several years, the Lord has been teaching my husband and me the Hebrew roots of our Christian faith. We were not really looking for it. He just began revealing it to us, little by little, in a myriad of ways. We began studying the Hebrew language, the Biblical feasts and thus began reading the Bible with new eyes. We both felt we have been led down to the roots of our faith, where it all began. Here we have discovered a richness that has revitalized our faith from the ground up.

As mentioned earlier, one of the enemy's schemes is to change times and seasons and laws. (Dan 7:25) In addition, Yeshua (Jesus' name in Hebrew) reveals to us the enemy *also* wants to steal, kill and destroy us.

"The thief comes only to steal and kill and destroy. I came that they may have life, and have it abundantly."
(John 10:10)

The enemy is a thief, a killer and destroyer.
One thing he wants to steal from us is our true identity. Why would he want to do that?
He wants to choke our root system and divert us from Yeshua, the Root of Jesse. (Isa 11:10)

Staying connected to our roots is vital.
Just as the Lord has opened many Jewish eyes to discover Yeshua
as Messiah, many Christians are discovering and embracing their Hebrew roots.
Jew and Gentile coming together as one new man, just like the apostle Paul said.

"For He Himself is our peace, who made both groups into one and broke down the barrier of the dividing wall, by abolishing in His flesh the enmity, which is the Law of commandments contained in ordinances, so that in Himself, He might make the two into **one new man**, *thus establishing peace, and might reconcile them both in one body to God through the cross, by it having put to death the enmity." (Eph 2:14-16)*

While discovering our roots, one particular treasure I have unearthed is the Hebrew calendar. What a gift it has been to find and explore. A few years ago, I decided to add the Hebrew months and appointed times to my Gregorian monthly planner. I thought it would be a practical way to get in His timing with my own life and schedule. I made a journal section and wrote the monthly characteristics, recorded my prayers and praises for the month and saw how His prophetic timing was manifesting in my life. Let me testify to you, it has been mind-blowing, faith-building and amazing! As I started tracking my life according to His timepiece, the Lord began to use it to confirm my steps according to His word and great love for me.

"Trust in the Lord with all your heart and do not lean on your own understanding.
In all your ways acknowledge Him and He will make your paths straight." (Pro 3:5-6)

You can only imagine what my monthly planner started to look like! Covered with loads of hand-written numbers, cross-referencing, color-coding and doodling, it became quite a conversation starter. For as often as I flipped open my planner, I couldn't help but tell others about His calendar. Finally, after a few years of creating my own handwritten monthly calendar and journal, I began to look online to see if I could purchase one. Lo and behold, I found nothing. And hence, I was given my next assignment. I really had no idea where to start. This seems to be a common theme with projects He has given me. I believe He likes it that way, for this has kept me humble and totally dependent on Him. As always, He has been faithful to the end.

I am blessed to release this fifth edition of "His Appointed Times."
I pray you find the new updates and features of this version to be valuable tool as you walk with Him.
Most of all, I pray that connecting with His calendar connects you closer to the Ancient of Days Himself!
"Abide in Me and I will abide in you." (Jn 15:4)

How To Use This Book

The main purpose of this calendar and journal is to bring awareness of the Lord's calendar and discover its application in our personal lives. His calendar is not an old way of "keeping time in the Bible days" but a living and active timepiece for us today. His calendar in our hands is a very practical tool to use as a reference and to record how His prophetic timing is manifesting in our lives.

At the start of this year's edition, gain insight and encouragement on the chapter on the new year 5781. Following, you will find a chapter for each Biblical month that includes seven teaching components. Let's look briefly at each teaching component and discover how to use the book.

Monthly Narrative

At the start of each monthly chapter, you will find a narrative for the month. These updated monthly narratives will give an overview and will highlight specific characteristics of the month. After reading, take some time to ponder over the questions posed at the end of the reading.

Monthly Journal

Opposite the monthly narrative, you will find the monthly journal. Use this section to record your thoughts, prayers and praises for the month. Be sure to write out, declare and meditate on any scriptures the Lord has brought to your attention. Record ways you have seen His prophetic timing unfolding in real-time in your life, big or small.

Monthly Chalkboard Teaching

Next you will find a visual teaching component, the monthly "Chalkboard Teaching." Gain additional insight as you watch the chalkboard teaching for the month. Find these teachings on the "Chalkboard Teachings" page on my website, www.christinevales.com. Use space below the image of the chalkboard to record notes and revelation.

Monthly Prophetic Fact Sheet

After the chalkboard teaching, you will find a chock filled monthly prophetic fact sheet. Facts include the appointed times of the month, prophetic monthly characteristics, Hebrew letter, tribe and more. Be sure to review the "Monthly Prophetic Fact Sheet" on page 6, which explains each section in further detail.

Monthly Calendar With Appointed Times

As you continue, you will find the calendar of the month. Note the calendar is based on the Hebrew month (in blue) while the Gregorian calendar (in red) is overlaid on top of it. All of the appointed times for the month are indicated on the calendar. Be sure to add personal appointments or significant dates happening in your life and see how they fall on His calendar and timing. To gain a better understanding on how the Lord established and measures time by the day, week, month and year, don't miss "Keeping Time With Adonai" on page 5.

Monthly Bible Study & Thought Questions

Dive into the New Testament for further reflection and gain fresh revelation through a Bible study on the theme of the month. Ponder thought questions for personal reflection, meditation and group study.

Monthly Bible Portions

Each monthly chapter concludes with Bible portions for each month. Keep in time with the annual reading through the Torah (first five books of the OT). Each portion is named by the opening words of the passage and is connected to the Hebrew calendar. Also find readings from the Prophets and New Testament and space for notes.

Don't Miss These Additional Features

Get to "Know Your Aleph-Bet" and gain prophetic insight in the Hebrew letters on page 8. On page 7, find "A Few More Gleanings." Learn how to add God's calendar on your smartphone, discover your birthday on His calendar and more! Lastly, end the year recording highlights in the new "Year In Review" on page 146.

As the days pass, note how His prophetic timing is unfolding in your life. Remind yourself of the monthly divine appointments, characteristics and promises from His word over your life. In addition, look back at past months, review your life in hindsight and see how His timing and promises have manifested in your life. You will be amazed!

Let's stay connected! Add your email to my list at www.christinevales.com. Consider subscribing to my YouTube channel and follow me as I follow Him on Facebook for the most up-to-date calendar posts and encouragements!

Scan QR codes to instantly connect with me on Facebook YouTube www.christinevales.com

Keeping Time With Adonai

Take some time to review this outline and learn how the Lord established and measures time by the day, week, month and year. Also note prophetic insights for 5781 & 5782.

HEBREW CALENDAR
- Hebrew calendar (noted in blue) is based on the sun and moon
- Gregorian calendar (noted in red) is based on the sun

*"Then God said, 'Let there be **lights** in the expanse of the heavens to separate the day from the night, and let them be for signs and for **seasons** and for **days** and **years** and let them be for lights in the expanse of the heavens to give light on the earth' and it was so." (Gen 1:14-16)*

HEBREW DAY (Yom)
- Begins at sundown and ends at sundown on the following day
  Example: Shavu'ot (Feast of Weeks)
  Is noted on the calendar on Sivan 6, 5781 = May 17, 2021
  Holiday actually starts at sundown, Sunday, May 16, 2021
  Holiday ends at sundown, Monday, May 17, 2021

*"Then God said, 'Let there be light' and there was light. God saw that the light was good and God separated the light from the darkness. God called the light day and the darkness He called night. And there was **evening** and there was morning, one day." (Gen 1:3-5)*

HEBREW WEEK (Shabua)
- All the days of the week are numbered
- Yom Rishon= 1st Day, Yom Sheni= 2nd Day, etc.
- The Hebrew week begins on Yom Rishon (1st Day)
- The Hebrew week ends with Yom Shabbat (The Sabbath)

THE SABBATH (Yom Shabbat)
- The seventh day of the week is given a name, "Yom Shabbat"
- "Yom Shabbat" means "Day to Cease or Rest"
- Shabbatot (Plural Shabbat) are most important days of year (Lev 26:35)
- Shabbat "start" and "end" are highlighted in blue
- ◦◦ Appears next to the beginning of each weekly Shabbat and represents the two Shabbat candles lit to enter Shabbat
- ◦ Appears next to the ending of each weekly Shabbat and represents the Havdalah (separation) candle lit to close Shabbat
- Shabbat is a picture of the shalom we can experience 24/7 when we receive the Prince of Peace in our hearts (Matt 11:28-30, Heb 4)
- Shabbat is a gift to man from The Lord
- Shabbat is not meant to be a burden to man, but a joy
- Sign of covenant between the Lord & His people (Ex 31:16-17)
- Time to remember the Lord's salvation (Deut 5:15)
- He calls us to remember the Sabbath and to keep it holy
- He calls us to rest from our normal work and meet with Him
- Shabbat in Him brings refreshment, reflection and direction

*"**Remember** the Sabbath day, to keep it **holy**. Six days you shall labor and do all your work, but the seventh day is a Sabbath of the Lord your God. In it, **you shall not do any work**, you or your son or your daughter, your male or you female servant or your cattle or your sojourner who stays with you. For in six days the Lord made the heaven and the earth, the sea and all that is in them and rested on the seventh day. Therefore the Lord **blessed the Sabbath day and made it holy**." (Exo 20:8-11)*

*"Jesus said to them, 'The **Sabbath was made for man,** and not man for the Sabbath. So the Son of Man is Lord even of the Sabbath.'" (Mark 2:27-28)*

HEBREW MONTH (Chodesh)
- The Hebrew month begins with the sighting of the new moon
- "Rosh Chodesh" means "Head of The Month"
- Day to cease (a Shabbat) and thank Him for His faithfulness
- Time to gather together and blow the shofar (ram's horn)
- Time to present first fruit offerings, offer praise and prayer
- Time to gain prophetic insight for the month ahead
- ○ Represents the new moon, Rosh Chodesh
- ● Represents the full moon, "Fullness" of the month
- Rosh Chodesh "start" and "end" are highlighted in yellow

*"Sing for joy to God our strength. Shout joyfully to the God of Ya'akov (Jacob). Raise a song, strike the timbrel, the sweet sounding lyre with the harp. Blow the trumpet at the **new moon**, at the full moon, on our feast day (Passover). For it is a statute for Yisra'el (Israel), an ordinance of the God of Ya'akov (Jacob)." (Ps 81:1-4)*

HEBREW YEAR (Shanah)
- There are essentially two "New Years" on the Hebrew calendar
- Physical / Civil New Year in Tishrei / Rosh Hashanah
- Spiritual New Year in Nissan / Rosh Chodashim
- See below…

ROSH HASHANAH ("Head of The Year")
- Starts on Tishrei 1 (9.7.21)
- Physical New Year, Based on the day of creation
- Civil New Year, Numerical year advances (5781 to 5782)
- This edition includes years 5780- 5782 (2020 – 2022)

ROSH CHODASHIM ("Head of The Months")
- Starts on Nissan 1 (3.14.21)
- Spiritual New Year, Based on our redemption at Passover/Cross

*"Now the LORD said to Moses and Aaron in the land of Egypt, 'This month shall be the **beginning of months** for you. It is to be the **first month** of the year to you." (Exo 12:1-2)*

5781 PROPHETIC INSIGHT Tishrei 1 - Elul 29, 5781 (9.19.20 - 9.6.21)
Hebrew Letter: Pey = 80
- A Mouth, Opening, Entrance, Word
- To Command, Speak, Open, To Be Present/Here
- A Divine Beginning of a New Order

Hebrew Letter: Alpeh = 1
- Ox, Bull, Leader, Who or What is First, Adonai
- Strength, Gentle, To Tame or Teach

*5781 •A Year to Lead By His Word

5782 PROPHETIC INSIGHT Tishrei 1 - Elul 29, 5782 (9.7.21- 9.25.22)
Hebrew Letter: Pey = 80
- A Mouth, Opening, Entrance, Word
- To Command, Speak, Open, To Be Present/Here
- A Divine Beginning of a New Order

Hebrew Letter: Bet = 2
- A House, Tent, The Body, Household
- Inside, Within

*5782 •A Year To Declare His Word Over Your Home & Body

Monthly Prophetic Fact Sheet

Each month has it's own "Prophetic Fact Sheet" which is a detailed outline of the characteristics of the month. This page describes and breaks down each section of the fact sheet. Be sure to review this page, as it will give you greater understanding as you review each month.

BABYLONIAN NAME
Babylon names were established for months when Israel was in captivity. Many of these names are noted in scripture. (Exo 13:4, Neh 6:15, Es 9:19) In this section, you will find each month's Babylonian name and meaning.

HEBREW NAME
The Lord ordered the months by number in relation to the first month of months, Nissan. (Exo 12:1-2) He called out Nissan to be the first month of months, as it marked our redemption at Passover. You will often see this notation in scripture. (ie: 2 Chron 31:7) Some months have Hebrew names as well as numbers and are noted here.

MONTH OF THE YEAR
This section shows the month's position in relation to the Spiritual Year (from Nissan) and the Physical /Civil Year (from Tishrei). The Hebrew Letters corresponding to the numerical value of each month are listed to reveal pictures and prophetic insight.

SEASON (Moed)
This section shows the season or "moed" at a glance. The spiritual year starts in Spring (Aviv) followed by Summer (Kaitz), Fall (Stav) and Winter (Horef). Find the themes for the season, months and tribes listed here.

APPOINTED TIMES (Moedim)
The Lord's divine appointments or "moedim" for the month are listed in this section. Find the Hebrew name of each appointed time with its English translation and date on the Hebrew calendar. Scripture references and other notes are also listed.

COLOR/GEMSTONE
There is a color and gemstone associated with each Hebrew month. The monthly color and gemstone are found in this section.

TRIBE OF ISRAEL
A tribe of Israel is connected to each month. This section lists the tribe's Hebrew name, meaning, lineage and Ya'kov's (Jacob's) prophetic blessing. The tribe's flag is described as well as its position in the encampment in the wilderness. Additional characteristics of the tribe are also listed here.

HEBREW LETTER
A Hebrew letter has been assigned to each month. This section shows the Hebrew letter, its position within the Hebrew alphabet, numerical value, as well as pictures and actions it represents.

ACTION/BODY PART
There is an action and body part that correspond with each Hebrew month. Find the physical and spiritual meaning in this section.

CONSTELLATION
A constellation is associated with each Hebrew month. Its purpose is to declare the glory of God. *Astronomy* supports the Gospel. *Astrology* is the counterfeit. In this section, the Hebrew name of the constellation is given as well as its meaning and characteristics. *"The heavens declare the glory of God and the firmament proclaims the work of His hands. Day to day pronounces a decree; and night-to-night proclaims knowledge. Are they not speeches and are they not words, of which is not their utterance heard? To every land their sound has gone forth and their doctrines to the limits of the world. In the sun He placed His tabernacle."* (Ps 19:1-4, Septuagint)

MONTHLY CHARACTERISTICS
Both Rabbinical and Biblical studies have shown there are certain and distinct characteristics unique to each month of the Hebrew calendar. This section lists those monthly characteristics, themes, etc. Also noted are scriptures connected with the theme of the month for you to read, meditate upon and declare over your life.

A Few More Gleanings

MONTHS & HOURS REFERENCE

MONTHS OF PHYSICAL YEAR
Based on Creation

1	**TISHREI**
2	CHESHVAN
3	KISLEV
4	TEVET
5	SH'VAT
6	ADAR
7	**NISSAN**
8	IYAR
9	SIVAN
10	TAMMUZ
11	AV
12	ELUL

MONTHS OF SPIRITUAL YEAR
Based on Redemption at Passover

1	**TISHREI**
2	CHESHVAN
3	KISLEV
4	TEVET
5	SH'VAT
6	ADAR
7	**NISSAN**
8	IYAR
9	SIVAN
10	TAMMUZ
11	AV
12	ELUL

COUNTING HOURS IN THE BIBLE

1st hour = 7am	7th hour = 1pm
2nd hour = 8am	8th hour = 2pm
3rd hour = 9am	9th hour = 3pm
4th hour = 10am	10th hour = 4pm
5th hour = 11am	11th hour = 5pm
6th hour = 12Noon	12th hour = 6pm

Note: Jesus was nailed to the cross on the 3rd hour and gave up His Spirit on the 9th hour. He suffered six hours on the cross for our redemption. Six is "Vav" and is a picture of a nail and number of man.
See Mark 15:25-39

OTHER FUN WAYS TO CONNECT WITH GOD'S CALENDAR

DISCOVER YOUR BIRTHDAY ON GOD'S CALENDAR

GO TO
"Hebcal.com"

SELECT
"Date Converter"

ENTER
Your birthday on the Gregorian Calendar

SELECT
"After Sunset" if you were born after sunset

SELECT
"Convert to Hebrew"

LOOK UP
Your birthday in the calendar and see what month and day it falls on

READ & PRAY ABOUT
Your birthday month and receive revelation about the appointed time when you were born

LOOK UP
Other significant dates in your life and see where they fall on His prophetic timepiece

GET SMART & GET GOD'S CALENDAR ON YOUR SMARTPHONE

GO TO
"Settings"

SELECT
"Calendar"

SELECT
"Alternate Calendars"

SELECT
"Hebrew"

The calendar on your smartphone will now display both the Hebrew and Gregorian calendars. (Instructions for Iphone)

Know Your "Aleph-Bet"

There is much prophetic insight to be gained by learning the 22 letters of the Hebrew "Aleph-Bet" or alphabet. Each letter has a numerical value, pictures and actions associated with it. Enjoying studying this Hebrew Aleph-Bet chart. Read as you would Hebrew, from right to left.

HEI= 5	DALET= 4	GIMEL= 3	BET/VET= 2	ALEPH= 1
5th Letter	4th Letter	3rd Letter	2nd Letter	1st Letter
"H"	"D"	"G"	"B" or "V"	"Silent"
Grace, Wind, Breath of God	Door, Path	Camel, Provision	House, Tent	Ox, Bull, The Leader
Window, Lattice	Way of Life	Something Lifted Up, To Rise	The Body	Strength, Gentle, Tame
To Behold, Reveal, Show	Movement Into or Out Of	Pride, Self-Will	Household or Family	What/Who is First, Adonai
Holy Spirit, The One Revealed	Creativity	Trinity	Inside, Within, Amid	To Teach
Man w/ Arms Raised in Praise				

YOD= 10	TET= 9	CHET= 8	ZAYIN= 7	VAV= 6
10th Letter	9th Letter	8th Letter	7th Letter	6th Letter
"Y"	"T"	"CH" or "KH"	"Z"	"V" or "W"
Closed Hand, Humility	Letter with a CHOICE: Life or Death	New Beginnings	Perfection, Completion	Man's Efforts
Mercy From The Hand of God	Fruitful Basket, Womb	Doorway, Threshold	To Rest, Nourish, Feed	Number of Man
Divine Order, Tithe, Testiony	Life, Fruit of the Spirit	Private Chamber, Heart, Fence	Plough, Sword, Weapon	Tent Peg, Hook, Nail
Done Deed, Finished Work	-OR- To Surround, Twist, Death	To Protect, Separate	To Pierce, Cut Off	Link, Connection
Smallest Letter in Alpeh-Bet	Snake Twisted in a Basket	Letter of Life		To Link, Connect, Secure, Add

SAMEKH= 60	NUN= 50	MEM= 40	LAMED= 30	KAF= 20
15th Letter	14th Letter	13th Letter	12th Letter	11th Letter
"C" or "S" Sharp	"N"	"M"	"L"	"K"
To Trust, Support	Messiah	Water, Mighty	Shepherd's Staff, Authority	Palm of Hand
To Lean Upon, Assist	Jubilee, Restoration	Massive, Chaos	To Teach, Point, Prick	Wing to Cover
To Come Full Circle	Offspring, Son, Seed, Heir, Fish	Like The Deep Waters	To Goad, Prod Forward	To Open Hand to Bless
To Prop Up, Uphold	Fish Moving, Activity, Life	To Flow As Water Downstream	Governmental Order, Tongue	Power to Bless or Supress
Slow Twisting, Turning Aside	To Sprout, Continue, Faithfulness		Tallest Letter in Aleph-Bet	Crown on Head of Bowed King

RESH= 200	QOF= 100	TSADE= 90	PEY= 80	AYIN= 70
20th Letter	19th Letter	18th Letter	17th Letter	16th Letter
"R"	"Q" or "K"	"TS" or "S" Sharp	"P" of "F"	"Guttural"
Head Person, Chief	Back of Head	Fish Hook	Mouth, Opening	Eye, Spring, Well, Fountain
What Is The Highet	Circuit of Time, To Go Around	Something Inescapable	Entrance, Beginning	To Look, See, Watch
Top of Something	Season, Cycle, Year	To Hunt, Capture, Harvest	To Command, Speak, Open	To Know, Understand, Obey
Most Important	What is Behind, Last, Final	To Pull Forward, Control	To Create with Words	To Focus Upon, To Be Seen
	The Least	Righteous, Humble	Here, Present	Appearance

			TAV= 400	SIN/SHIN= 300
			22nd Letter	21st Letter
			"TH" or "T"	"S" or "SH"
			Mark, Sign, Cross, An "X"	Teeth, Ivory
			To Join Two Things, Seal	Point of Rock, Peak
			Convenant, The Last	Something Sharp
			Ownership	To Devour, Consume, Destroy
				El Shaddai

His Appointed Times

Hebrew / Gregorian Calendar
Journal & Study Guide

Discover The Lord's Prophetic Calendar
In Real-Time In Your Life

December 2020 thru January 2022

"'Listen! Behold, a sower went out to sow.
And it happened, as he sowed, that some seed fell by
the wayside and the birds of the air came and devoured it.

Some fell on stony ground where it did not have
much earth and immediately it sprang up because it
had no depth of earth. But when the sun was up it was
scorched and becacuse it had not root- it withered away.

And some seed fell among thorns and the thorns
grew up and choked it and it yielded no crop.

But other seed fell on good ground and yielded a
crop that sprang up, increased and produced some
thirtyfold, some sixty, and some a hundred.'

And He said to them,
'He who has ears to hear, let him hear!'"

Mark 4:3-9

5781

"Lead By His Word"

September 19, 2020 – September 6, 2021

5781 New Year to "Lead By His Word"

As we study the Lord's calendar we will discover there are essentially two "New Years."
One occurs in the fall on Tishrei 1 and is based on the creation of the world. It is likened
to the physical birth of the earth. It is also known as Rosh Hashanah, literally "Head of The Year."

The second occurs in the spring on Nissan 1 and is based on our redemption
at Passover, foreshadowing Jesus' death, burial and resurrection.
This is likened to the spiritual birth of the world. (Exo 12)

This section highlights the physical new year, when the numerical year turns over on the civil calendar.
This year, the year advanced from 5780 into 5781. The Lord has great encouragement for us as we cross
over into the new year and bids us to continue on as His mouthpieces in the "Decade of Declaration."

We can gain spiritual understanding as we look into the prophetic pictures embedded in the year.
Dig into the "Prophetic Fact Sheet" below and listen to the "Chalkboard Teaching" on the new year 5781.
Receive fresh revelation and use space below the chalkboard to jot down notes on opposite page, 13.

Let's continue abiding in Him and His word so we can lead others by His word and to His Word- Jesus!

Prophetic Fact Sheet for the New Year 5781

HEBREW YEAR 5781
- Physical Year / Civil Year
- Based on The Creation of The World
- Coincides with Gregorian Year 2020/ 2021
- 5780's follows 5770's, "Decade of Vision"

BEGINS AND ENDS
- Tishrei 1, 5781 – Elul 29, 5781
- September 19, 2020 – September 6, 2021

THEME OF 5781
- "Lead By His Word"

HEBREW LETTERS

PEY
- 17th Letter of the Hebrew Alphabet
- Numerical Value 80
- A Mouth, Opening, Entrance
- To Command, Speak, Declare, Open
- Letter with Two Forms

ALEPH
- 1st Letter of the Hebrew Alphabet
- Numerical Value 1
- An Ox, Father, God
- Strong Gentle Leader
- To Lead, Teach
- Silent Letter

SCRIPTURES TO CHEW ON AND DECLARE
- **Exo 4:12** Now therefore go and I will be with your mouth and teach you what to say.
- **Jer 1:7** Do not say, "I am a youth", because everywhere I send you, you shall go and all that I command you, you shall speak.
- **Ps 81:10** Open your mouth wide and I will fill it.
- **Prov 17:28** Even a fool is counted wise when he holds his peace. When he shuts his lips, he is considered perceptive.
- **Prov 31:8-9** Open your mouth for the speechless, in the cause of all who are appointed to die. Open your mouth, judge righteously and plead the cause of the poor and needy.
- **Prov 31:26** She opens her mouth with wisdom and on her tongue is the law of kindness.
- **2 Tim 4:2** Preach the word. Be ready in season and out of season. Reprove, rebuke, exhort with great patience and instruction.
- **Heb 4:12** For the word of God is living and powerful and sharper than any two-edged sword, piercing even to the division of soul and spirit and joints and marrow and is a discerner of the thoughts and intents of the heart.

KEY VERSES OF THE DECADE 5780
- **Matt 12:34** For out of the abundance of the heart the mouth speaks.
- **Prov 18:21** Death and life are in the power of the tongue. And those who love it will eat its fruit.

 Scan QR code to go directly to "Chalkboard Teachings" page at www.christinevales.com.

13

Tevet 5781

December 16, 2020 – January 13, 2021

Tenth Month of Spiritual Year
29 days

Growing Up in Tevet

As the youngest child in my family I always wanted to be older. I saw all the privileges my older brothers had. I wanted in. I just wasn't old enough or allowed to do things they were able to do. They could stay up late... while I had to go to bed. They could drive... while I had to ride my bike. They were tall enough to go on the big roller coasters... while I went on the kiddie rides. How I longed to "be big." I thought to myself... "Will there ever come a day when I will grow and do all that 'fun stuff'?" The answer soon came, and before I knew it, I was old enough to drive and go on the "big" rides. What I didn't realize was there was a whole lot of other "stuff" that comes with "being big." Growth means responsibility and servitude. That my friends, is what this month of Tevet is all about... growing up!

The word Tevet means "good" and growth is good. The Lord is there to help us grow. Sure there are growing pains, but as the word says... it is used for maturity. (Heb 12:11) Situations that test our faith and maturity will present themselves, however, in these situations He is present and will never allow more than we can handle. He doesn't leave us alone in the process. He illuminates our path as soon as we step into Tevet, as the candles of the menorah still burn bright from Chanukah. They are a reminder of His Word being a lamp onto our feet and a light onto our path as we grow in Him. (Ps 119:105)

A big part of growth is perspective. Two people can look at the same situation and one sees encouragement while the other sees defeat. It's all how we look at things. The Jews call this the battle of our "good eye" versus our "evil eye." The Lord highlights the importance of vision this month and calls us to see with our "good eye", to see things from His heavenly perspective. This is underscored in this month's Hebrew letter, "Ayin", which depicts an eye and is associated with vision and focus. It's a great time to ask the Lord to bring our lives into His focus and priorities. This may include reviewing our education to see where He is calling us to advance or remain steady in our current position. He is calling us to meditate on His promises and those prophetic words He spoke over us and to be encouraged in His truth and love and move forward in His purpose for us. What are you focusing on this month? What are you imagining for the month ahead? Is this bringing you fear or peace? Bring Him your plans and allow His perfect love to cast out all fear as He orders your steps. You will begin to see things from His vantage point and experience His wisdom, peace, rest and most of all His love.

The tribe of Dan is connected with Tevet and instills valuable lessons on maturity. The name Dan means "to judge or rule." This alone requires maturity. Dan was positioned as the rearguard of the Lord's army as they moved in the wilderness and in battle. They were strong warriors and knew how to take down their enemy without even touching them. This is foretold in Jacob's prophecy over him... *"Dan shall judge his people as one of the tribes of Israel. Dan shall be a serpent in the way as a horned snake in the path that bites the horse's heels so that his rider falls backward." (Gen 49:16-17)* Wow! Now that's what I call moving in your gift! Yet, not everyone in this tribe moved in his calling. Samson was from the tribe of Dan and was called to be a deliverer of Israel. However, Samson did not submit or grow in the Lord. Samson allowed his passions to control him. In the end, after losing his strength and sight, Samson finally submitted his will to the Lord. In his last and final battle, he brought down pillars, knocking down the enemy without even touching them, but losing his life in the process. May we submit to the Lord's call over our lives, that we may grow in Him, learn His ways, and bring deliverance to others.

Lastly, getting our emotions under control is another sign of maturity. If we're in battle this month, anger may arise in us, but the Word says we can be angry "but sin not." (Eph 4:26). He empowers us by His Spirit to do so. Let's allow the fruit of the Spirit within us to have dominion over our flesh!

So are you ready to "be big?" Now is the time! Ask the Lord which areas of your life growth is needed. Write them down and be encouraged in Him. This seed you plant will reap rewards of maturity. Is this not what growth is about? Are you allowing your "evil eye" to rule over you? Ask the Lord to show you His heavenly perspective. Are you facing a battle? "Be angry... but sin not" by tapping into His Sprit within you. The Lord will surely show you strategies to take down the enemy without even touching him, like Dan. Take time get His vision on moving forward in maturity in your work, ministry, education, etc. May He "grow you up" this month so you can say what Paul said... *"When I was a child, I used to speak like a child, think like a child, reason like a child. When I became a man, I did away with childish things." (1 Cor 13:11)*

Journal for Tevet 5781

Use the space below to record your thoughts, praises and prayers for this month.

Chalkboard Teaching for Tevet 5781

Go to "Chalkboard Teachings" page at www.christinevales.com or scan QR Code below.
Enjoy watching the chalkboard teaching for this month. Use space below to take notes.

Scan QR code to go directly to "Chalkboard Teachings" page at www.christinevales.com.

18

Prophetic Fact Sheet for Tevet 5781

BABYLONIAN NAME
TEVET
- "Good", "Divine Grace"
- From Hebrew "Tov" = Good

HEBREW NAME
NONE

MONTH OF THE YEAR
10th MONTH OF SPIRITUAL YEAR
- Hebrew Letter Yod – 10
- A Closed Hand, Appointed Mercy from The Hand of God
- An Action, Work, Humility, Holiness, Godly Authority
- Number of Order, Tithe, Testimony

4th MONTH OF PHYSICAL/CIVIL YEAR
- Hebrew Letter Dalet = 4
- A Door, Path, The Way of Life, Creativity

SEASON (Moed)
HOREF (Winter)	• Season of Victory & Joy
TRIBES of HOREF	• Dan, Asher, Naftali

THEMES of HOREF
TEVET	• Maturing in Him
SH'VAT	• His Righteousness is My Foundation
ADAR	• His Joy is My Strength

APPOINTED TIMES (Moedim)
TEVET 1	**ROSH CHODESH TEVET** (Head of Month, Tevet)
	• Ps 81:1-4
KISLEV 24-	**CHANUKAH** (Feast of Dedication)
TEVET 3	• Jn 10:22
TEVET 10	**ASARAH B'TEVET** (Tevet 10)
	• Minor Fast Day
	• Nebuchadnezzar's siege of Jerusalem 587 BC
	• 2 Kings 25:1-2, Eze 33:21, Zech 8:19

COLORS/GEMSTONES
COLORS	Dark Blue, Turquoise
GEMSTONES	Sapphire, Turquoise

TRIBE OF ISRAEL
DAN
- "To Rule", "Judge", "Grow Up", "Mature"
- 5th Son of Ya'akov (Jacob)
- 1st Son by Rachel's Maid, Bilhah (Gen 30:4-6)

Ya'akov's Prophetic Blessing (Gen 49:16-18) *"Dan shall judge his people, as one of the tribes of Yisra'el. Dan shall be a serpent in the way, a horned snake in the path that bites the horse's heels, so that his rider falls backward. For Your salvation I wait, O LORD."*
- Camped north of tabernacle w/Asher & Naftali (Num 2)
- Flag: Black and white with a serpent (Gen 49:17)
- Could take down the enemy w/o touching them (Jdg 16)

HEBREW LETTER

AYIN
- 16th Letter of the Hebrew Alphabet
- Numerical Value 70
- Perfection, Spiritual Order
- An Eye, Spring, Well
- To Watch, Know, Understand, Obey, Focus On

ACTION/BODY PART
ANGER	• Be angry but sin not (Gal 5, Eph 4:26)
LIVER	• Fasting purifies the blood

CONSTELLATION
GEDI (Capricorn)
- The Goat, The Cut Off, Offering
- Goat was sin offering for Israel (Lev 10:16-17)
- Jesus our Scapegoat/Perfect Atoning Sacrifice (Heb 9-10)

MONTHLY CHARACTERISTICS
- Month of growing up (1 Cor 13:11, Heb 12:11)
- Follow His lead on the path to your destiny (Prov 4:18)
- Month to get focused (Hab 2:2)
- Time to get priorities in order (Prv 16:3,9)
- Let His Word to be a lamp onto your feet (Ps 119:105)
- Declare His promises over your life (Ps 119:49)
- Review prophetic words (Deut 28:1-14, 2Cor 1:20)
- Review education for your next phase of life (Prv 1-4)
- Keep your eyes fixed on Jesus (2 Cor 4:18, Heb 12:2)
- See w/ your good eye/ War against evil eye (Matt 6:22-23)
- Evaluate from your seat in heavenly places (Eph 2:6)
- His eyes seek to support those whose heart is His (2 Chron 16:9)
- "Holy anger"/ Be angry but sin not (Gal 5, Eph 4:26)
- Stand for your inheritance (Dan 12:13)
- Leap out of fear and passivity (2 Tim 1:7)
- Put on your armor and stand (Eph 6:10-18, Jas 4:7)
- Pray for new artistic expressions in worship
- Pray for your commander in chief and authority figures
- Consider fasting/ Brings body into order (Matt 4:4)
- Capitalize on downtime to study His Word (2 Tim 2:15)
- Gregorian year ends

Tevet 5781
<u>Bible Study & Thought Questions</u>
For Individual & Group Study

Dive into this portion of the New Testament for further reflection on the theme of the month. Ponder thought questions that follow and use space for personal reflection and group study.

Luke 2:39-52

39 When they had performed everything according to the Law of the Lord, they returned to Galilee, to their own city of Nazareth. **40** The Child continued to grow and become strong, increasing in wisdom; and the grace of God was upon Him.

41 Now His parents went to Jerusalem every year at the Feast of the Passover. **42** And when He became twelve, they went up there according to the custom of the Feast; **43** and as they were returning, after spending the full number of days, the boy Jesus stayed behind in Jerusalem. But His parents were unaware of it, **44** but supposed Him to be in the caravan, and went a day's journey; and they began looking for Him among their relatives and acquaintances. **45** When they did not find Him, they returned to Jerusalem looking for Him. **46** Then, after three days they found Him in the temple, sitting in the midst of the teachers, both listening to them and asking them questions. **47** And all who heard Him were amazed at His understanding and His answers. **48** When they saw Him, they were astonished; and His mother said to Him, "Son, why have You treated us this way? Behold, Your father and I have been anxiously looking for You." **49** And He said to them, "Why is it that you were looking for Me? Did you not know that I had to be in My Father's house?" **50** But they did not understand the statement which He had made to them. **51** And He went down with them and came to Nazareth, and He continued in subjection to them; and His mother treasured all these things in her heart. **52** And Jesus kept increasing in wisdom and stature, and in favor with God and men.

Thought Questions for Tevet 5781

In these passages of Luke 2, where were Jesus and his parents going? How were His actions and words mature? (Read Psalm 119:99)

_____
_____
_____
_____
_____

Luke 2:40 reads, "The Child continued to grow and become strong, increasing in wisdom; and the grace of God was upon Him."   How do you think we can increase in wisdom?

_____
_____
_____
_____
_____

Where did Jesus' parents finally find Jesus, and what was Jesus doing when they found Him? How does this speak to our priorities in our everyday lives?

_____
_____
_____
_____
_____

Jesus listened and asked questions as a young boy on God's word. How are you spending your time developing God's word in your heart, as Jesus did? (v 46)

_____
_____
_____
_____
_____

In this month of growing up, if Jesus continued to grow in wisdom, how much more should we? What areas of your life is the Lord highlighting where you need to mature in?

_____
_____
_____
_____
_____

Tevet 5781

Sunday	Monday	Tuesday	Wednesday
Yom Rishon (1st Day)	Yom Sheni (2nd Day)	Yom Sh'lishi (3rd Day)	Yom Revi'i (4th Day)
		KISLEV 29 DEC 15 ✡Chanukah 🕯🕯🕯🕯🕯🕯 (Feast of Dedication, Day 6) ◐Rosh Chodesh TEVET	1 DEC 16 ◐Rosh Chodesh TEVET ✡Chanukah 🕯🕯🕯🕯🕯🕯🕯 (Feast of Dedication, Day 7)
5 DEC 20	6 DEC 21	7 DEC 22	8 DEC 23
12 DEC 27	13 DEC 28	14 ●DEC 29	15 DEC 30
19 JAN 3	20 JAN 4	21 JAN 5	22 JAN 6
22 JAN 10	27 JAN 11	28 JAN 12	29 JAN 13 ◐Rosh Chodesh SH'VAT

December 2020/January 2021

Thursday	Friday	Saturday	Moed
Yom Chamishi (5th Day)	Yom Shishi (6th Day)	Yom Shabbat (The Shabbat)	Season
2 DEC 17 ✡Chanukah 🕯🕯🕯🕯🕯🕯🕯🕯 (Feast of Dedication, Day 8)	**3** DEC 18 ✡Chanukah Ends (Feast of Dedication) 🕯🕯 *Shabbat begins*	**4** DEC 19 🕯 *Shabbat ends*	**Horaf (Winter)** *Season of Victory & Joy*
9 DEC 24	**10** DEC 25 ✡Asarah B'Tevet (10th of Tevet) ✝Christmas (Christian Date Celebrating Yeshua's Birth) 🕯🕯*Shabbat begins*	**11** DEC 26 🕯 *Shabbat ends*	**Months of Horaf** Tevet *Maturing in Him* Sh'vat *His Righteousness is My Foundation* Adar *His Joy is My Strength*
16 DEC 31	**17** JAN 1 🔔New Year's Day 2021 (New Year Begins on Gregorian Calendar) 🕯🕯 *Shabbat begins*	**18** JAN 2 🕯 *Shabbat ends*	**Tribes of Horaf** Dan *To Rule, To Judge, To Mature* Asher *Pleasure, Happinesss, Delicious* Naftali *Sweetness to me*
23 JAN 7	**24** JAN 8 🕯🕯 *Shabbat begins*	**25** JAN 9 🕯 *Shabbat ends*	**Notes**

Bible Portions for Tevet 5781

Read through the Torah in a year and glean from the Prophets and the New Testament.
Space provided for notes.

Week of:
Tevet 4, 5781/ Dec 19, 2020

Torah Portion: **Miketz** *(At the end of)* Gen 41:1- 44:17
Prophets Portion: 1 Kings 3:15- 4:1
NT Portion: 1 Cor 2:1- 5

_____

_____

_____

_____

_____

_____

Week of:
Tevet 11, 5781/ Dec 26, 2020

Torah Portion: **Vayigash** *(And he drew near)* Gen 44:18- 47:27
Prophets Portion: Eze 37:15- 28
NT Portion: Luke 6:9- 16

_____

_____

_____

_____

_____

_____

Week of:
Tevet 18, 5781/ Jan 2, 2021

Torah Portion: **Vayechi** *(And he lived)* Gen 47:28- 50:26
Prophets Portion: 1 Kings 2:1- 12
NT Portion: 1 Pet 1:3- 9

_____

_____

_____

_____

_____

_____

Week of:
Tevet 25, 5781/ Jan 9, 2021

Torah Portion: **Shemot** *(Names)* Exo 1:1- 6:1
Prophets Portion: Isa 27:6- 28:13, 29:22- 23
NT Portion: Acts 7:17- 29

_____

_____

_____

_____

_____

_____

Sh'vat 5781

January 14 – February 12, 2021

Eleventh Month of Spiritual Year
30 days

Be Like a Tree in Sh'vat

"How blessed is the man who does not walk in the counsel of the wicked, nor stand in the path of sinners, nor sit in the seat of scoffers. But his delight is in the law of the Lord and in His law he meditates day and night. He will be like a tree firmly planted by streams of water which yields its fruit in its season and its leaf does not wither and in whatever he does, he prospers." (Ps 1:1-3) This is the Lord's picture of a blessed man or woman. The Lord is reminding us in this month of Sh'vat… to be like this tree. Let us learn as we turn our gaze upon the tree in Psalm 1 and taste the fruit of its branches.

What does it mean to be a blessed man or woman? Psalm 1 tells us those who delight and meditate on God's Word are blessed. Just a reminder… blessed means "favor." Who doesn't want favor? There are people who think God wants us to be miserable, but that's the devil's desire, not God's! God gives us the secret to health, prosperity and favor in His Word. In the natural, reading the Bible seems like the last place you would go to find these things. But there is a secret here! The Lord uses the foolish things of the world to shame the wise. (1 Cor 1:27) He says, if we read and meditate upon His word, it will bring us delight and peace. How can a book make someone joyful? Ah, because the Bible is no ordinary book. It is the Word of God. The Book of Life. It is living and active and Yeshua is the Word itself. True peace is found in Him. As it is written… *"In the beginning was the Word, and the Word was with God, and the Word was God. He was in the beginning with God. All things came into being through Him, and apart from Him nothing came into being that has come into being. In Him was life, and the life was the Light of men." (Jn 1:1-4)* When we believe His Word, which is Jesus Himself, we become a child of God and receive the very spirit of God living in us. His Spirit within us teaches us and is our very life and true peace.

As we continue reading, we see blessed is the man who is firmly planted. Being established brings security. Having roots that go deep brings stability. Prosperity comes when we are rooted in Him. When we are rooted in righteousness we will not be moved. (Prv 12:3) What does that mean? Righteousness means to be in "right standing" with God. None of us are born in right standing with God. There is only One who came on our behalf to redeem us so we can be in right standing with Him. His name is Jesus, Yeshua - the Messiah. We could never obtain righteousness on our own. When Jesus shed His blood on the cross a divine exchange took place. He became sin who knew no sin that we may become His righteousness. (2 Cor 5:21) When we accept His blood, shed on our behalf, we immediately take on His righteousness. This right standing brings peace with God and a firm foundation in Him. Let's be encouraged by Paul's words *"… that you, being rooted and grounded in love, may be able to comprehend with all the saints what is the breadth and length and height and depth, and to know the love of Christ which surpasses knowledge, that you may be filled up to all the fullness of God." (Eph 3:17-19)*

Psalm 1 reveals the prosperity of this tree is also due to the fact that it is firmly planted by streams of water. A watered tree is a blessed tree. Likewise, a watered man is a blessed and prosperous man. These are not just any streams, but "living waters." In Hebrew "mayim chaim" is a picture of the Spirit of God. His Spirit within us brings true refreshment, shalom and favor to our body, mind and soul. The role and power of the Holy Spirit within us is even highlighted in the heavens this month. The constellation Aquarius, "The Water Bearer', reminds us as believers, to tap into the power of His Spirit within us and offer His living waters of refreshment to others. The heavens truly declare the glory of the Lord!

As Psalm 1 concludes, we learn the blessed tree is fruitful. It does not wither and is prosperous in all its ways. How is a tree prosperous? A prosperous tree bears fruit and its leaves do not wither because it is properly connected and nourished by its source of life. It stands firm in storms. It provides shelter and shade for others. That is the picture of a blessed man. A fruitful man. A rooted man. It has been said, the fruit is in the root. The Root of Righteousness is Christ Himself. Rooted in Him, we will bear much fruit that will last.

Do you long to be like the tree in Psalm 1? Check your positioning! Spend time reading His word and discover how meditating on His word, like Psalm 1, brings blessing. Are you bearing good fruit? Be mindful of what you're reading and listening to. We are known by our fruit. Abiding in Him, the fruit of the Spirit will be evident and come forth automatically in our lives. *"The fruit of the Spirit is love, joy, peace, patience, kindness, goodness, faithfulness, gentleness, self-control." (Gal 5:22-23)* In Sh'vat, go forth in your true identity in Him, as a favored, secure, prosperous and blessed man or woman who, like the "Psalm 1 tree", brings refreshment and shade to others!

Journal for Sh'vat 5781

Use the space below to record your thoughts, praises and prayers for this month.

_____
_____
_____
_____
_____
_____
_____
_____
_____
_____
_____
_____
_____
_____
_____
_____
_____
_____
_____
_____
_____
_____
_____
_____
_____
_____
_____
_____
_____
_____
_____
_____
_____

Go to "Chalkboard Teachings" page at www.christinevales.com or scan QR Code below.
Enjoy watching the chalkboard teaching for this month. Use space below to take notes.

Scan QR code to go directly to "Chalkboard Teachings" page at www.christinevales.com.

28

Prophetic Fact Sheet for Sh'vat 5781

BABYLONIAN NAME
SH'VAT •Meaning Unknown

HEBREW NAME
NONE

MONTH OF THE YEAR
11th MONTH OF SPIRITUAL YEAR
•Hebrew Letters Yod and Aleph = 11
•Disorder, Imperfection, Incompleteness, Unfulfillment

5th MONTH OF PHYSICAL/CIVIL YEAR
•Hebrew Letter Hei = 5
•Wind, Breath, Window, Lattice, Grace, Praise
•Behold, The One revealed

SEASON (Moed)
HOREF (Winter) •Season of Victory & Joy

TRIBES of HOREF •Dan, Asher, Naftali

MONTHLY THEMES of HOREF
TEVET •Maturing in Him
SH'VAT •His Righteousness is My Foundation
ADAR •His Joy is My Strength

APPOINTED TIMES (Moedim)
✿**SH'VAT 1** **ROSH CHODESH SH'VAT** (Head of Month, Sh'vat)
•Ps 81:1-4

✿**SH'VAT 15** **TU' B'SH'VAT** (The New Year for Trees)
•Sh'vat 15

COLORS/GEMSTONES
COLOR Light Olive Green, Yellow
GEMSTONES Citrine Quartz, Peridot

TRIBE OF ISRAEL
ASHER •"Pleasure", "Happiness", "Delicious", "Fatness", "Favor"
•8th Son of Ya'akov (Jacob)
•2nd Son by Le'ah's Maid, Zilpah (Gen 30:12-13)

Ya'akov's Prophetic Blessing (Gen 49:20) *"As for Asher, his food shall be rich and he will yield royal dainties."*
•Camped north of tabernacle w/Dan & Naftali (Num 2)
•Flag: Beige with an olive tree (Gen 49:20)
•Inherited some of the most fertile territory in Israel

HEBREW LETTER

TSADE
•18th Letter of the Hebrew Alphabet
•Number of Life, "L'Chaim" in Hebrew
•Numerical Value 90
•Fishing Hook, Something Inescapable
•That which has control
•To Hunt, Capture, Harvest, Pull Forward
•Humble letter positioned in humble worship
•Jehovah Tsidkenu = The Lord is Our Righteousness
•Jer 23:6

ACTION/BODY PART
TASTE •Eat The Word, Drink Living Water (Matt 4:4, Jn 6:35)
•Taste and see the Lord is good (Ps 34:8)
STOMACH & ESOPHAGUS

CONSTELLATION
DELI (Aquarius)
•The Water Carrier
•Believers /The Temple of The Holy Spirit (1 Cor 6:19)
•Roots awaken to Living Waters, Jesus Himself (Jn 4)

MONTHLY CHARACTERISTICS
•Righteousness is your foundation
•Hebrew "Tsidkenu"= Righteousness
•New Year for Trees
•Develop plan of sustaining the generations
•Meditate on Psalm 1
•Connect with the "trees" in your life (Tu' B'Sh'vat)
•Consider who is planted in your field?
•Are the trees in your field ready to bear fruit?
•Month the almond tree blossoms in Israel (Jer 1)
•He is watching over His word to perfom it (Jer 1:12)
•See wagons of water coming to quench your thirst as seen in Old & New Test (Gen 24:10-27, Mk 14:13-14)
•You may need to be watered in a new way
•Evaluate your positioning (John 15)
•Shout "My blessings are on the way!"
•Taste & meditate on the life of His word (John 6:63)
•Good month to read the book of Daniel
•Beware of the delicacies of the king (Dan 1:5, 8)
•Consider doing a Daniel fast this month
•God may reveal a new way of eating after fasting
•"Eat The Word" (Jer 15:16, Eze 3:3, Prov 13:25)

Sh'vat 5781
Bible Study & Thought Questions
For Individual & Group Study

Dive into this portion of the New Testament for further reflection on the theme of the month.
Ponder thought questions that follow and use space for personal reflection and group study.

Matthew 7:15-20

[15] "Beware of the false prophets, who come to you in sheep's clothing, but inwardly are ravenous wolves. [16] You will know them by their fruits. Grapes are not gathered from thorn bushes nor figs from thistles, are they? [17] So every good tree bears good fruit, but the bad tree bears bad fruit. [18] A good tree cannot produce bad fruit, nor can a bad tree produce good fruit. [19] Every tree that does not bear good fruit is cut down and thrown into the fire. [20] So then, you will know them by their fruits.

John 15:1-11

"I am the true vine, and My Father is the vinedresser. [2] Every branch in Me that does not bear fruit, He takes away; and every branch that bears fruit, He prunes it so that it may bear more fruit. [3] You are already clean because of the word which I have spoken to you. [4] Abide in Me, and I in you. As the branch cannot bear fruit of itself unless it abides in the vine, so neither can you unless you abide in Me. [5] I am the vine, you are the branches; he who abides in Me and I in him, he bears much fruit, for apart from Me you can do nothing. [6] If anyone does not abide in Me, he is thrown away as a branch and dries up; and they gather them, and cast them into the fire and they are burned. [7] If you abide in Me, and My words abide in you, ask whatever you wish, and it will be done for you. [8] My Father is glorified by this, that you bear much fruit, and so prove to be My disciples. [9] Just as the Father has loved Me, I have also loved you; abide in My love. [10] If you keep My commandments, you will abide in My love; just as I have kept My Father's commandments and abide in His love. [11] These things I have spoken to you so that My joy may be in you, and that your joy may be made full.

Thought Questions for Sh'vat 5781

In the passages of Matthew, what method does Jesus give us to discern if a tree is good or bad? How do we apply this to people or things in our lives?

_____

_____

_____

_____

_____

_____

Describe an experience when you have used your discernment while inspecting the fruit of another.

_____

_____

_____

_____

_____

_____

After meditating on John 15, what does it mean to abide in Him?   Describe ways you abide in Him?

_____

_____

_____

_____

_____

_____

In this month of trees, how would you describe yourself? Watered? Planted? Dried? Fruitful? How did you get that way?

_____

_____

_____

_____

_____

What fruit have you produced by abiding in Him?

_____

_____

_____

_____

_____

Sh'vat 5781

Yom Rishon (1st Day)	Yom Sheni (2nd Day)	Yom Sh'lishi (3rd Day)	Yom Revi'i (4th Day)
Sunday	Monday	Tuesday	Wednesday
			TEVET 29 JAN 13 ◯Rosh Chodesh SH'VAT
4 JAN 17	5 JAN 18	6 JAN 19	7 JAN 20
11 JAN 24	12 JAN 25	13 JAN 26	14 JAN 27
18 JAN 31	19 FEB 1	20 FEB 2	21 FEB 3
25 FEB 7	26 FEB 8	27 FEB 9	28 FEB 10

January/February 2021

Yom Chamishi (5th Day)	Yom Shishi (6th Day)	Yom Shabbat (The Shabbat)	Moed
Thursday	**Friday**	**Saturday**	**Season**
1 JAN 14 ☾Rosh Chodesh SH'VAT	2 JAN 15 ♙♙ *Shabbat begins*	3 JAN 16 ♙ *Shabbat ends*	**Horaf (Winter)** *Season of Victory & Joy*
8 JAN 21	9 JAN 22 ♙♙ *Shabbat begins*	10 JAN 23 ♙ *Shabbat ends*	**Months of Horaf** Tevet *Maturing in Him* Sh'vat *His Righteousness is My Foundation* Adar *His Joy is My Strength*
15 ●JAN 28 ✡Tu B'Sh'vat (15th of Sh'vat) (New Year for Trees)	16 JAN 29 ♙♙ *Shabbat begins*	17 JAN 30 ♙ *Shabbat ends*	**Tribes of Horaf** Dan *To Rule, To Judge, To Mature* Asher *Pleasure, Happinesss, Delicious* Naftali *Sweetness to me*
22 FEB 4	23 FEB 5 ♙♙ *Shabbat begins*	24 FEB 6 ♙ *Shabbat ends*	**Notes**
29 FEB 11	30 FEB 12 ☾Rosh Chodesh ADAR ♙♙ *Shabbat begins*		

Bible Portions for Sh'vat 5781

Read through the Torah in a year and glean from the Prophets and the New Testament.
Space provided for notes.

Week of:
Sh'vat 3, 5781/ Jan 16, 2021

Torah Portion: **Va'era** *(And I appeared)* Exo 6:2- 9:35
Prophets Portion: Eze 28:25- 29:21
NT Portion: Rom 9:14- 24

_____

_____

_____

_____

_____

_____

Week of:
Sh'vat 10, 5781/ Jan 23, 2021

Torah Portion: **Bo** *(Enter)* Exo 10:1- 13:16
Prophets Portion: Jer 46:13- 28
NT Portion: 1 Cor 11:20- 34

_____

_____

_____

_____

_____

_____

Week of:
Sh'vat 17, 5781/ Jan 30, 2021

Torah Portion: **Beshalach** *(When he let go)* Exo 13:17- 17:16
Prophets Portion: Judg 4:4- 5:31
NT Portion: John 6:22- 40

_____

_____

_____

_____

_____

_____

Week of:
Sh'vat 24, 5781/ Feb 6, 2021

Torah Portion: **Yitro** *(Jethro)* Exo 18:1- 20:26
Prophets Portion: Isa 6:1- 7:6, 9:5- 6
NT Portion: Heb 12:18- 24

_____

_____

_____

_____

_____

_____

Adar 5781

February 13 – March 13, 2021

Twelfth Month of Spiritual Year
29 days

Go Out With Joy In Adar

Adar is the last month on the Lord's spiritual calendar. The word "Adar" means strength and we are encouraged to finish the year strong, but not in our own striving, for strength is not found in our might or knowledge. The word reveals our real strength is found in the joy of the Lord! Nehemiah 8:10 tells us the joy of the Lord is our strength. It may seem like a funny way to gain strength, but the Lord's ways are truly higher than ours. David's lyrics testify… "in His presence is fullness of joy!" (Ps 16:11) When we spend time in His presence, He fills us with His joy. When we have His joy, we have His strength, which is much better than our own. Let's now dig in and discover His joy in Adar!

The month of Adar is known as the most joyful month of the year. It has a history of being a month of good fortune celebrating the Lord's victory over evil. These attributes burst forth in the feast of Purim. Purim is a joyful feast commemorating the amazing defeat of evil Haman's plot to massacre the entire Jewish race in 357 BC. The captivating story is told in the book of Esther and is a "must read" this month. Here's a quick overview… During the Babylonian captivity of the Jews, King Xerxes of Persia was searching for a new queen. Word got out to Mordecai, a well-known Jew, who insisted his beautiful niece, Hadassah, enter this "royal beauty pageant." He gave her a new name, Esther, to protect her Jewish identity. She agreed and was sequestered for months in the King's harem and eventually was selected as the new queen of Persia. During Esther's reign, Mordecai notified her of an edict, calling for a total extermination of the Jews on Adar 13. Mordecai informed her of the dark heart of Haman, King's Xerxes right-hand man, who created and sealed this evil plot with the King's ring. Once sealed, this edict could not be expunged. Haman hated the Jews, especially Mordecai. Mordecai ordered the Jews to fast and pray and summoned Esther to approach the King and reveal her identity for "such a time as this." Approaching the King in those days, even for a queen, could cost someone their life. Esther fasted and prayed and was received by the King. She prayerfully invited both the King and Haman to two feasts, and at the second one, she revealed her identity as a Jew and exposed the evil Haman. The King ordered Haman to be hung and appointed Mordecai to his cabinet. Although the edict could not be changed, King Xerxes issued a second edict declaring the Jews can fight against their enemies. On Adar 13, instead of being slaughtered, the Jews defended themselves and lived! To celebrate this tremendous victory in the Lord, the feast of Purim was established and is gregariously enjoyed to this day!

The Lord calls us to find strength in His joy and rise up in our authority and courage, like Mordecai and Esther. They both found their strength and strategies in the presence of the Lord. Let us magnify the Lord and not the giants in the land. Watch Him turn our fears to laughter! (Prov 31:25) It's a time to reveal our true identity, just as Esther did. It's time to take off our mask and be authentic with others, especially with the Lord. When we remove our masks before Him, our true identity in Him is uncovered, and our destiny as victors springs forth. Masks stop joy. Transparency brings light and life.

Adar is a time to develop war strategies against the enemy. We may think we have the answer to defeat our foe, but true wisdom is found in His presence. His strategies outwit the enemy. Praise, fasting and prayer are not "normal" tactics for most armies, however, this is no ordinary army. This is the army of the Lord of Hosts. May we be sensitive to His voice and obedient to His specific instructions in Adar.

Last, but definitely not least, the story of Esther reminds us the Lord has reversed the curse over our lives. Christ became a curse for us so we could take on His righteousness. (Gal 3:13) Therefore all of His promises are yes and amen as believers. (2 Cor 1:20) When a curse is reversed, you are like a doe let loose! These are the exact prophetic words spoken over the tribe of this month, Naphtali. (Gen 49:21) Naphtali's name means "sweetness to me." When you are set free from a curse it sure is sweet! Let us rise the sweetness of our salvation and use our authority to condemn any words rise up against us in judgment and declare the truth - His word over our lives!

As you wrap up the last month of the spiritual year, invest time in the joy of His presence and you will end the year strong. Read through the book of Esther and ask the Lord to speak to you through it's pages. May you rise up, throw off fear and laugh at the days to come. Enter into Purim on Adar 14 and celebrate how Jesus' death, burial and resurrection reversed every curse over your life. Leap like Naphtali and go out in joy and be led forth in the peace as you arise in your true royalty and authority… for such a time as this! (Isa 55:12)

Journal for Adar 5781

Use the space below to record your thoughts, praises and prayers for this month.

_____

_____

_____

_____

_____

_____

_____

_____

_____

_____

_____

_____

_____

_____

_____

_____

_____

_____

_____

_____

_____

_____

_____

_____

_____

_____

_____

_____

_____

_____

_____

_____

_____

_____

_____

_____

_____

_____

_____

Chalkboard Teaching for Adar 5781

Go to "Chalkboard Teachings" page at www.christinevales.com or scan QR Code below.
Enjoy watching the chalkboard teaching for this month. Use space below to take notes.

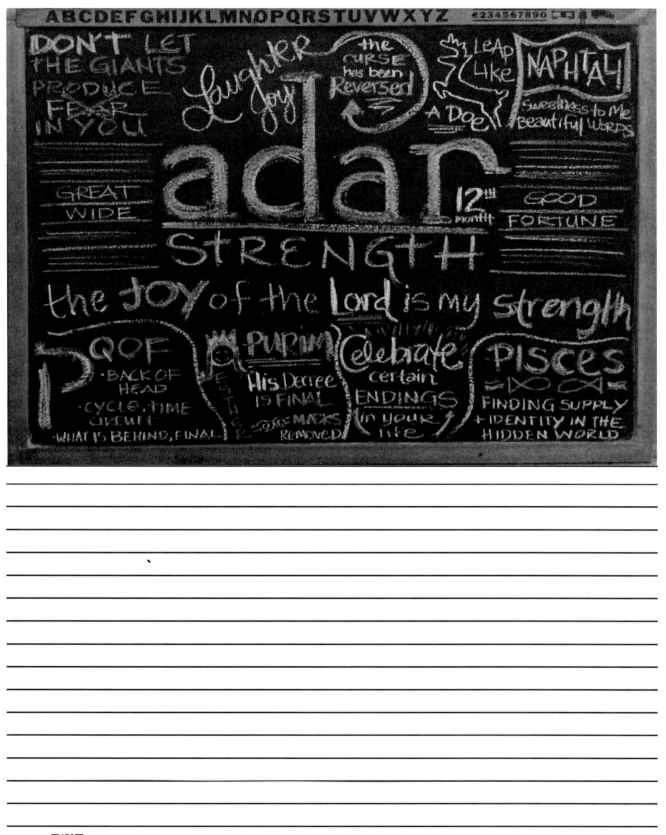

 Scan QR code to go directly to "Chalkboard Teachings" page at www.christinevales.com.

Prophetic Fact Sheet for Adar 5781

BABYLONIAN NAME

ADAR
•"Strength", "Good Fortune", "Magnificent"

An additional month of Adar is added in a Hebrew leap year.
1st Adar is "pregnant" with 2nd Adar

HEBREW NAME
NONE

MONTH OF THE YEAR

12th MONTH OF SPIRITUAL YEAR
•Hebrew Letters Yod and Bet = 12
•Leadership, Government

6th MONTH OF PHYSICAL/CIVIL YEAR
•Hebrew Letter Vav = 6
•A Tent Peg, Nail
•To Connect, Make Secure
•Man's Efforts

SEASON (Moed)

HOREF (Winter) •Season of Victory & Joy

TRIBES of HOREF •Dan, Asher, Naftali

MONTHLY THEMES of HOREF
TEVET •Maturing in Him
SH'VAT •His Righteousness is My Foundation
ADAR •His Joy is My Strength

APPOINTED TIMES (Moedim)

ADAR 1 ✿ROSH CHODESH ADAR (Head of Month)
•Ps 81:1-4

ADAR 13 ✿TA'ANIT ESTHER (Fast of Esther)
•Es 9:17

ADAR 14 ✿PURIM (Feast of Lots)
•Es 9:17,22,28
•Prov 16:33

ADAR 15 ✿SHUSHAN PURIM (Feast of Lots in Shushan)
•During days of Esther, Purim was celebrated one day later in Shushan/ Also in Jerusalem
•Es 9:18

✿Something to Note... In Hebrew Leap Years, Purim is celebrated in 2nd Adar to properly connect with Passover

COLOR/GEMSTONE

COLOR Purple

GEMSTONE Amethyst

TRIBE OF ISRAEL

NAFTALI (Naphtali) •"Sweetness to me"
•6th Son of Ya'akov
•2nd Son by Rachel's Maid, Bilhah (Gen 30:7-8)

• **Ya'akov's Prophetic Blessing** (Gen 49:21) *"Naphtali is a doe let loose, He gives beautiful words*
•Camped north of tabernacle w/Dan and Asher (Num 2)
•Flag: Fuchsia pink with a leaping doe (Gen 49:21)

HEBREW LETTER

QOF
•19th Letter of the Hebrew Alphabet
•Numerical Value 100
•Holiness, Redemption
•What is Behind, Final, The Least, Back of Head
•Season, Cycle, Year, Circuit of Time, To Go Around

ACTION/BODY PART

LAUGHTER •Good medicine (Prov 17:22, 31:25)

SPLEEN •Filters blood- balances bodily fluids

CONSTELLATION

DAGIM (Pisces)
•Two Fish
•Find supply in hidden world/ His Word (Matt 17:24-27)
•Meditate on true ID /Hidden in Him (Ps 32, Col 1:27, 3:3)

MONTHLY CHARACTERISTICS

•Most joyous month/ Celebrate God's victory over evil
•Celebrate certain endings in your life (Eccles 7:8)
•Communicate like Esther (Ex 4:12, Es 4:16, Ps 81:10)
•Enter into joy and laughter (Prov 31:25)
•God ordains your fear to laugh (1 John 4:18)
•Tap into His supernatural joy within you (Gal 5:22-23)
•Read the book of Esther this month
•Remove masks/ Masks stop joy (Es 4:15-16, 7:1-6)
•Awaken to true authority & leadership in Him (Rom 8:37)
•Walk in true position of authority/ royalty in Him (Gal 4:7)
•Spiritual awakening brings physically awakening (3 Jn 2)
•The joy of the Lord is your strength (Neh 8:10)
•In His presence is fullness of joy (Ps 16:11)
•Condemn every tongue that rises against you (Isa 54:17)
•Thanksgiving releases His supply (Matt 14:13-21)
•Don't let the giants produce fear in you (1 John 4:18)
•Guard your heart from idolatry (Prov 4:23)
•Celebrate the curse is overturned (Es 7:9-10)
•Jesus became a curse for us (Gal 3:13)
•Despair breaks meditating upon His love (1 Jn 4:18)
•Remove cloak of heaviness for garments of praise (Ps 30)
•Last month of spiritual year / Finish strong in His joy
•Go out with joy and be led forth with peace (Isa 55:12)
•You have been created for such a time as this (Es 4:14)

Adar 5781
Bible Study & Thought Questions
For Individual & Group Study

Dive into this portion of the New Testament for further reflection on the theme of the month. Ponder thought questions that follow and use space for personal reflection and group study.

Philippians 3:12-16

[12] Not that I have already obtained it or have already become perfect, but I press on so that I may lay hold of that for which also I was laid hold of by Christ Jesus. [13] Brethren, I do not regard myself as having laid hold of it yet; but one thing I do: forgetting what lies behind and reaching forward to what lies ahead, [14] I press on toward the goal for the prize of the upward call of God in Christ Jesus. [15] Let us therefore, as many as are perfect, have this attitude; and if in anything you have a different attitude, God will reveal that also to you; [16] however, let us keep living by that same standard to which we have attained.

Philippians 4:4-9

[4] Rejoice in the Lord always; again I will say, rejoice! [5] Let your gentle spirit be known to all men. The Lord is near. [6] Be anxious for nothing, but in everything by prayer and supplication with thanksgiving let your requests be made known to God. [7] And the peace of God, which surpasses all comprehension, will guard your hearts and your minds in Christ Jesus.

[8] Finally, brethren, whatever is true, whatever is honorable, whatever is right, whatever is pure, whatever is lovely, whatever is of good repute, if there is any excellence and if anything worthy of praise, dwell on these things. [9] The things you have learned and received and heard and seen in me, practice these things, and the God of peace will be with you.

Thought Questions for Adar 5781

In the passages in Philippians 3:12-16, what is the one thing Paul puts his focus on?

_____
_____
_____
_____
_____
_____

What is the benefit of forgetting what lies behind and pressing forward?

_____
_____
_____
_____
_____
_____

In this last month of the spiritual year, where is your focus? Are you looking back or ahead?

_____
_____
_____
_____
_____
_____

In this month of joy, what instruction does the Lord give you to do always? How do you do this practically?

_____
_____
_____
_____
_____
_____

How does thinking on the precious things in Philippians 4:8 affect your joy? What have you been thinking on?   How can you train and guide your mind to think on these things?

_____
_____
_____
_____
_____
_____

Adar 5781

Yom Rishon (1st Day)	Yom Sheni (2nd Day)	Yom Sh'lishi (3rd Day)	Yom Revi'i (4th Day)
Sunday	**Monday**	**Tuesday**	**Wednesday**
2 FEB 14	3 FEB 15	4 FEB 16	5 FEB 17
9 FEB 21	10 FEB 22	11 FEB 23	12 FEB 24
16 FEB 28	17 MAR 1	18 MAR 2	19 MAR 3
23 MAR 7	24 MAR 8	25 MAR 9	26 MAR 10

February/March 2021

Yom Chamishi (5th Day)	Yom Shishi (6th Day)	Yom Shabbat (The Shabbat)	Moed
Thursday	Friday	Saturday	Season
	SH'VAT 30 FEB 12 ○ Rosh Chodesh ADAR ♊ Shabbat begins	**1** FEB 13 ○ Rosh Chodesh ADAR ♒ Shabbat ends	**Horaf (Winter)** *Season of Victory & Joy*
6 FEB 18	**7** FEB 19 ♊ Shabbat begins	**8** FEB 20 ♒ Shabbat ends	**Months of Horaf** Tevet *Maturing in Him* Sh'vat *His Righteousness is My Foundation* Adar *His Joy is My Strength*
13 FEB 25 ✡Ta'anit Esther (Fast of Esther)	**14** FEB 26 ✡Purim (Feast of Lots) ♊ Shabbat begins	**15** ●FEB 27 ✡Shushan Purim (Feast of Lots in Shushan) ♒ Shabbat ends	**Tribes of Horaf** Dan *To Rule, To Judge, To Mature* Asher *Pleasure, Happinesss, Delicious* Naftali *Sweetness to me*
20 MAR 4	**21** MAR 5 ♊ Shabbat begins	**22** MAR 6 ♒ Shabbat ends	**Notes**
27 MAR 11	**28** MAR 12 ♊ Shabbat begins	**29** MAR 13 ♒ Shabbat ends ○ Rosh Chodashim (Head of The Months)	

Bible Portions for Adar 5781

Read through the Torah in a year and glean from the Prophets and the New Testament.
Space provided for notes.

Week of:
Adar 1, 5781/ Feb 13, 2021

Torah Portion:	**Mishpatim** *(Judgements)* Exo 21:1- 24:18
Prophets Portion:	Jer 34:8- 22, 33:25- 26
NT Portion:	Matt 5:38- 42

_____

_____

_____

Week of:
Adar 8, 5781/ Feb 20, 2021

Torah Portion:	**Terumah** *(Offerings)* Exo 25:1- 27:19
Prophets Portion:	1 Kings 5:12- 6:13
NT Portion:	Heb 9:1- 10

_____

_____

_____

Week of:
Adar 15, 5781/ Feb 27, 2021

Torah Portion:	**Tetzavgh** *(You shall command)* Exo 27:20- 30:10
Prophets Portion:	Eze 43:10- 27
NT Portion:	Heb 13:10- 17

_____

_____

_____

Week of:
Adar 22, 5781/ Mar 6, 2021

Torah Portion:	**Ki Tisa** *(When you elevate the head)* Exo 30:11- 34:35
Prophets Portion:	1 Kings 18:1- 39
NT Portion:	1 Cor 8:4- 13

_____

_____

_____

Week of:
Adar 29, 5781/ Mar 13, 2021

Torah Portion:	**VaYakel** *(And he assembled)* Exo 35:1- 38:20
Prophets Portion:	1 Kings 7:13- 26, 40-50
NT Portion:	2 Cor 9:6- 11

Torah Portion:	**Pekudel** *(Accouting of)* Exo 38:21- 40:38
Prophets Portion:	1 Kings 7:51- 8:21
NT Portion:	2 Cor 3:7- 18

_____

_____

_____

_____

Nissan 5781

March 14 – April 12, 2021

First Month of Spiritual Year
30 days

Nissan... The Beginning of Miracles

"This month, Nissan, shall be the beginning of months for you. It is to be the first month of the year to you." (Ex 12:1-2) When we arrive at Nissan, we not only cross over into a new month, but also pass over into a new year. So... surprise! It's a new spiritual year! Is it really that surprising? Nissan begins the season of spring when evidence of new life starts to bloom around us. These physical evidences should open the eyes of our heart to discern His timing and seasons. Truly all of creation does declare the glory of God!

During the long winter months, it appears as if nothing will ever flower again. Most trees stand naked and grasses that were once green remain dormant for months. New life seems hopeless. Yet as Nissan appears, the voice of the Lord calls us saying... *"Arise, my darling, my beautiful one, come with me. Look! The winter is past and the rains are over and gone. Flowers appear on the earth. The season of singing has come. The cooing of doves is heard in our land. The fig tree forms its early fruit. The blossoming vines spread their fragrance. Arise, come, my darling, my beautiful one, come with me." (SOS 2:10-13)* In Nissan, the Lord is calling us to awake from the winter and arise into the season of new life... the season of spring!

When spring comes into full swing it's as if a miracle has occurred in the earth. In God's mercy it has indeed! In fact, the word Nissan means "the beginning of miracles!" The earth is being "redeemed" right before our eyes. This points us to the secret of the season. As Jesus said, *"Truly, truly, I say to you, unless a grain of wheat falls into the earth and dies, it remains alone, but if it dies, it bears much fruit." (Jn 12:24)* Jesus was referring to Himself before laying down His own life on Passover. His desire was to redeem us as well as all creation. He wants us to start the year in the best way possible and this begins with accepting His offer of redemption at Passover. Even the heavens point our hearts to His great redemption this month. The constellation Aries depicts a lamb, but not just any lamb, The Passover Lamb, Jesus. (Ps 19:1) The Israelites received redemption by applying the blood of the lamb over the doorposts of their homes and upon seeing it, the angel of death passed over them. This was a type and shadow of the redemptive power of the blood of Jesus. When we confess Jesus as our Lord, His blood is applied over the doorposts of our hearts. We become a new creation in Christ. (2 Cor 5:17) A miracle happens and new life begins. His desire is for us, His children, to know His love and mercies. Let's take a moment and meditate on this finished work- the redemptive blood of the Passover Lamb, Yeshua and new life in Him. (Heb 10 & 1 Pet 1:18-25)

Once we receive redemption by His blood, the miracles continue. Knowing we are "but dust" He graciously breathes the breath of His Holy Spirit into us. (Ps 103:14) This fresh wind of His Spirit is depicted through the fifth letter of the Hebrew alphabet connected to Nissan, called "Hei." Hei is a picture of the Spirit of God like wind blowing through a lattice or a window and has a value of five. Five represents grace. In His grace He revives us by His Holy Spirit so we can rise and bear fruit, just as He did when He was resurrected on First Fruits. Paul declares this truth to us in Romans, *"...if the Spirit of Him who raised Jesus from the dead is living in you, He who raised Christ from the dead will also give life to your mortal bodies because of His Spirit who lives in you." (Rom 8:11)*

In this month of redemption, the Lord is calling us to rise, walk and praise Him! Judah, the tribe connected with Nissan, shows us how to move *first* in praise. The body part and action associated with Nissan is very fitting- for we are called to "continuous walking" with our "right foot." Our right side is often referred to our spiritual side of trust. The Lord bids us to rise up and step with our best foot forward in faith. He instructs us to keep on walking with praise on our lips as we move onward and upward into our bright future in Him. This is what the Israelites did after the very first Passover. They followed the Lord's direction under Moses and boldly walked forward in faith out of Egypt. When they came to the Red Sea, He made a way through the waters and consumed their enemies... and the miracles continued.

After a long winter, we all need reviving. The Lord is the only one who can bring "springtime" to our souls. Have you been redeemed by the blood of the Passover Lamb, Yeshua? If not, take time to consider His personal gift for you. Start this new spiritual year with a clean heart. (1 Jn 1:7) If you already know the Lord as your Redeemer, take time during this Passover to remember how He redeemed you out of slavery. (Deut 15:15) You will experience new life in those fallow areas of your heart. Praise Him in this season of singing! (SOS 2:12) Proceed boldly with your right foot of faith and watch the His mighty hand work miracles before your eyes in Nissan! (Ex 6:6)

Journal for Nissan 5781

Use the space below to record your thoughts, praises and prayers for this month.

_____
_____
_____
_____
_____
_____
_____
_____
_____
_____
_____
_____
_____
_____
_____
_____
_____
_____
_____
_____
_____
_____
_____
_____
_____
_____
_____
_____
_____
_____
_____
_____
_____
_____
_____
_____

Go to "Chalkboard Teachings" page at www.christinevales.com or scan QR Code below.
Enjoy watching the chalkboard teaching for this month. Use space below to take notes.

Scan QR code to go directly to "Chalkboard Teachings" page at www.christinevales.com.

48

Prophetic Fact Sheet for Nissan 5781

BABYLONIAN NAME
NISSAN
- "Their Flight"
- From Hebrew "Nissim"= Miracles

HEBREW NAME
AVIV
- "Ripening of Barley Grain"

MONTH OF THE YEAR
1st MONTH OF SPIRITUAL YEAR
- Hebrew Letter Aleph = 1
- Beginning, Abba, Ox, Head, Unity, To Teach

7th MONTH OF PHYSICAL/CIVIL YEAR
- Hebrew Letter Zayin = 7
- Completion, Perfection, A Sword, Rest
- All 7's are important and dear to The Lord

SEASON (Moed)
AVIV (Spring)
- Season of Deliverance

TRIBES of AVIV
- Yehudah, Yisachar, Zvulun

MONTHLY THEMES of AVIV
- **NISSAN** · Month of Redemption
- **IYAR** · Month of Transition
- **SIVAN** · Month of Extravagant Provision

APPOINTED TIMES (Moedim)
NISSAN 1 · ✿ROSH CHODASHIM (Head of The Months)
- Exo 12:1-2

NISSAN 14 · ✿TA'ANIT BECHORIM (Fast of Firstborn Son)

NISSAN 14 · ✿EREV PESACH (Passover Eve)
- Exo 12

NISSAN 15 · ✿PESACH (Passover)
- Exo 12
- Messiah's Crucifixion (Matt 27:45-46)

NISSAN 15-21 · ✿CHAG HAMATZOT (Feast of Unleavened Bread)
- Messiah's Burial (Matt 27:57-61, 1 Cor 5:6)

NISSAN 16-SIVAN 6 · ✿SEFIRAT HaOMER (Counting The Omer)
- 50-day countdown to Shavu'ot (Pentecost)

NISSAN 16 · ✿REISHIT KATZIR (Firstfruits)
- Messiah's Resurrection (Matt 28:1-6)

NISSAN 26 · ✿YOM HaSHOAH (Holocaust Memorial Day)

Date to Note:
NISSAN 10 · ✿Day to bring Passover lamb into the house
- Ex 12

✿Day Jesus, the Lamb of God, entered into the house of God, Jerusalem ("Palm Sunday")
- Matt 21

COLORS/GEMSTONES
COLORS	Dark Red, Sky Blue
GEMSTONES	Garnet, Blue Topaz

TRIBE OF ISRAEL
YEHUDAH (Judah)
- "Praise of Adonai"
- 4th Son of Ya'akov
- 4th Son by Le'ah (Gen 29:35)

Ya'akov's Prophetic Blessing (Gen 49:8-12) *"Yehudah, your brothers shall praise you. Your hand shall be on the neck of your enemies. Your father's sons shall bow down to you. Yehudah is a lion's whelp. From the prey, my son, you have gone up. He couches, he lies down as a lion, and as a lion, who dares rouse him up? The scepter shall not depart from Yehudah nor the ruler's staff from between his feet until Shiloh comes, and to him shall be the obedience of the peoples. He ties his foal to the vine and his donkey's colt to the choice vine. He washes his garments in wine and his robes in the blood of grapes. His eyes are dull from wine and his teeth white from milk."*

- Camped east of tabernacle w/Yisachar & Zvulun (Num 2)
- Flag: Sky-blue with a lion (Gen 49:9)
- Moved forward first in praise (Judg 1)
- Functionally the firstborn of Israel (Gen 35:22, 34:25)
- Yeshua (Jesus) is The Lion of the tribe of Yehudah
- Hebrew root "Yadah" = To extend a hand in praise
- "Jew" comes from "Yehuda"= A people of praise
- He is enthroned on the praises of His people (Ps 22:3)
- Yehudah is The King of the tribes

HEBREW LETTER

HEI
- 5th Letter of the Hebrew Alphabet
- Numerical Value 5
- Grace, Wind, Breath, Window, Lattice
- Behold, The One revealed
- Man with arms raised, Violent Praise

ACTION/BODY PART
WALKING · Ongoing Progress, One step at a time

RIGHT FOOT
- Foot of Trust
- Spiritual Side (Isa 48:13)

CONSTELLATION
TALEH (Aries)
- The Lamb
- Celebrate the Passover Lamb (Jn 12, Rev 5:11-14)
- Heaven connecting with earth

MONTHLY CHARACTERISTICS
- Month of redemption
- The beginning of miracles
- Crossover into the new / Put your best foot forward
- Standing at your promised land/ Setting course for future
- Watch your speech (Matt 12:34)
- Speak life, praises and thanks (Prov 18:21)
- Thank God for where you came from (Ps 40)
- Month of praise / Go forth like Yehudah (Ps 100:4)
- Praise confounds the enemy (2 Chron 20:22)
- Time of cleansing/ Spring Cleaning (Jn 21:12)
- "New Year of Kings" (2 Sam 11:1) / Pray over politicians
- Pray over finances / Tax month in USA
- Month to "Learn to Fish" (Matt. 17:24-27)
- Month of the latter rains (Joel 2:23)

Nissan 5781
Bible Study & Thought Questions
For Individual & Group Study

Dive into this portion of the New Testament for further reflection on the theme of the month. Ponder thought questions that follow and use space for personal reflection and group study.

John 12:1-26

12 On the next day the large crowd who had come to the feast, when they heard that Jesus was coming to Jerusalem, **13** took the branches of the palm trees and went out to meet Him, and began to shout, "Hosanna! Blessed is He who comes in the name of the Lord, even the King of Israel." **14** Jesus, finding a young donkey, sat on it; as it is written, **15** "Fear not, daughter of Zion; behold, your King is coming, seated on a donkey's colt." **16** These things His disciples did not understand at the first; but when Jesus was glorified, then they remembered that these things were written of Him, and that they had done these things to Him. **17** So the people, who were with Him when He called Lazarus out of the tomb and raised him from the dead, continued to testify about Him. **18** For this reason also the people went and met Him, because they heard that He had performed this sign. **19** So the Pharisees said to one another, "You see that you are not doing any good; look, the world has gone after Him."

20 Now there were some Greeks among those who were going up to worship at the feast; **21** these then came to Philip, who was from Bethsaida of Galilee, and began to ask him, saying, "Sir, we wish to see Jesus." **22** Philip came and told Andrew; Andrew and Philip came and told Jesus. **23** And Jesus answered them, saying, "The hour has come for the Son of Man to be glorified. **24** Truly, truly, I say to you, unless a grain of wheat falls into the earth and dies, it remains alone; but if it dies, it bears much fruit. **25** He who loves his life loses it, and he who hates his life in this world will keep it to life eternal. **26** If anyone serves Me, he must follow Me; and where I am, there My servant will be also; if anyone serves Me, the Father will honor him.

Thought Questions for Nissan 5781

During what feast did Jesus come riding into Jerusalem?

_____

_____

_____

_____

Jesus came riding into the city on the 10th of Nissan, the same day the Israelites were instructed to take an unblemished lamb into their homes. (Ex 12) Have you taken the lamb of God into the home of your heart?

_____

_____

_____

_____

_____

_____

In John 12:23, Jesus says. "The hour has come for the Son of Man to be glorified." Compare to Mark 1:15. Why is this good news?

_____

_____

_____

_____

_____

_____

In this month of miracles, Jesus said "...unless a grain of wheat falls into the earth and dies, it remains alone; but if it dies, it bears much fruit." (v 24) What is that a picture of?

_____

_____

_____

_____

_____

Likewise, in Mark 4, Jesus compared the word of God to a seed. What is miraculous about a seed? If His word is in your heart what miracles can you expect?

_____

_____

_____

_____

_____

Nissan 5781

Yom Rishon (1st Day) Sunday	Yom Sheni (2nd Day) Monday	Yom Sh'lishi (3rd Day) Tuesday	Yom Revi'i (4th Day) Wednesday
1　　MAR 14 ○Rosh Chodashim (Head of The Months)	**2**　　MAR 15	**3**　　MAR 16	**4**　　MAR 17
8　　MAR 21	**9**　　MAR 22	**10**　　MAR 23 ✡Nissan 10 The Lamb in the house (Ex 12) Jesus enters Jerusalem (Matt 21)	**11**　　MAR 24
15　　●MAR 28 ✡Pesach (Passover) 📖Chag Hamatzot (Feast of Unleavened Bread, Day 1)	**16**　　MAR 29 ✡Sefirat HaOmer　Omer 1 (Counting The Omer: Nissan 16 - Sivan 6) ✡Reishit Katzir (Firstfruits) 📖Chag Hamatzot (Feast of Unleavened Bread, Day 2)	**17**　　MAR 30 Omer 2 📖Chag Hamatzot (Feast of Unleavened Bread, Day 3)	**18**　　MAR 31 Omer 3 📖Chag Hamatzot (Feast of Unleavened Bread, Day 4)
22　　APR 4 Omer 7 ✝Easter (Christian Date Celebrating Yeshua's Resurrection) **29**　　APR 11 Omer 14	**23**　　APR 5 Omer 8 **30**　　APR 12 Omer 15 ○Rosh Chodesh IYAR	**24**　　APR 6 Omer 9	**25**　　APR 7 Omer 10

March/April 2021

Yom Chamishi (5th Day)	Yom Shishi (6th Day)	Yom Shabbat (The Shabbat)	Moed
Thursday	**Friday**	**Saturday**	**Season**
		ADAR 29 MAR 13 *Shabbat ends* ○ Rosh Chodashim (Head of The Months)	**Aviv (Spring)** *Season of Deliverance*
5 MAR 18	6 MAR 19 *Shabbat begins*	7 MAR 20 *Shabbat ends*	**Months of Aviv** Nissan *Month of Redemption* Iyar *Month of Transition* Sivan *Month of Extravagant Provision*
12 MAR 25	13 MAR 26 *Shabbat begins*	14 MAR 27 ✿Ta'anit Bechorim (Fast of The Firstborn Son) ✿Erev Pesach (Passover Eve) *Shabbat ends*	**Tribes of Aviv** Yehuda *Praise of Adonai* Yisachar *Adonai Brings Reward* Zvulum *Dwelling Wished For*
19 APR 1 Omer 4 ▤Chag Hamatzot (Feast of Unleavened Bread, Day 5)	20 APR 2 Omer 5 ▤Chag Hamatzot (Feast of Unleavened Bread, Day 6) *Shabbat begins*	21 APR 3 Omer 6 ▤Chag Hamatzot (Feast of Unleavened Bread, Day 7) *Shabbat ends*	**Notes**
26 APR 8 Omer 11 ✿Yom HaShoah (Holocaust Memorial Day)	27 APR 9 Omer 12 *Shabbat begins*	28 APR 10 Omer 13 *Shabbat ends*	

Bible Portions for Nissan 5781

Read through the Torah in a year and glean from the Prophets and the New Testament.
Space provided for notes.

Week of:
Nissan 7, 5781/ Mar 20, 2021

Torah Portion: **VaYikra** *(And He called)* Lev 1:1- 5:26
Prophets Portion: Isa 43:21- 44:23
NT Portion: Heb 10:1- 18

_____
_____
_____
_____
_____
_____

Week of:
Nissan 14, 5781/ Mar 27, 2021

Torah Portion: **Tzav** *(Command)* Lev 6:1- 8:36
Prophets Portion: Jer 7:21- 8:3, 9:22- 23
NT Portion: Heb 8:1- 6

_____
_____
_____
_____
_____
_____

Week of: *Holiday Readings*
Nissan 21, 5781/ Apr 3, 2021

Torah Portion: Ex 33:12- 34:26, Num 28:19-25
Prophets Portion: Eze 36:37- 37:14
NT Portion: 1 Cor 5:6- 8

_____
_____
_____
_____
_____
_____

Week of:
Nissan 28, 5781/ Apr 10, 2021

Torah Portion: **Sh'mini** *(Eighth)* Lev 9:1- 11:47
Prophets Portion: 2 Sam 6:1- 7:17
NT Portion: Acts 10:9- 22, 34-35

_____
_____
_____
_____
_____
_____

Iyar 5781

April 13 – May 11, 2021

Second Month of Spiritual Year
29 days

Secrets of Transition in Iyar

"Are we there yet?" We've all said it. We've all heard it. It's that expression that rolls so easily off the tongue when we think... "Shouldn't we already be there by now?!" This happens during that "in-between" place called a transition. This is exactly where we find ourselves in Iyar, the second month on the Lord's spiritual calendar. Transitions can be scary times even testing times. But fear not! The Lord is near. As we draw near to Him, He will reveal secrets from His word and will order our steps through this transitional month.

The Bible reveals the Israelites found themselves smack in the middle of a transition in the month of Iyar. (Exo 13-19) It was just one month ago when the Lord miraculously delivered them from Egypt. Now they were on their way... but were not "there" yet! While in transit, we see them growing thirsty and hungry and soon in the midst of battle. Suddenly their praise quickly turned to complaints. When we find ourselves in a place of uncertainty we are very susceptible to murmuring and are quick to turn back to our old ways of doing things. But how can we keep from complaining and keep on praising in such trying times? The secret is in knowing the true nature of God and His unconditional love for us. It's here in this portion of scripture, where the Lord revealed His true character to the Israelites by revealing secrets hidden in His Name. Knowing who God really is and His great love for us will establish our hearts to trust Him and praise Him, even in times of testing.

"The name of the LORD is a strong tower, the righteous run in to it and is safe." (Prov 18:10) In Iyar, the Lord reveals Himself as *"Jehovah Raphe", "Jehovah Jireh"* and *"Jehovah Nissi."* The Lord delights in revealing Himself to us and it is here in this month of Iyar where He displayed His name as our Healer, our Provider and our Banner. These names reveal His faithfulness and His covenant to meet our physical and spiritual needs. The secret of running into His name establishes our hearts and stirs up faith to praise Him.

During a transitional time, we can feel overwhelmed and weighed down with extra burdens and worries. The Lord encourages us through the night sky this month in the constellation Taurus, which is a picture of a ruling ox. An ox is a strong animal who serves by carrying heavy burdens. The Lord is our strong Ox and He calls us to cast our cares upon Him because He cares for us. (Ps 84:7) When we roll our burdens onto Him, we are able to move easier, especially through this connecting month. It makes me think about bags and connections. Doesn't it feel good when someone offers to carry your bags... especially when you are trying to connect to another flight! Carrying bags can slow us down when trying to catch a connection. Why not allow Him to carry our bags and burdens so we can walk freely. Remember, His yoke is easy and burden is light. (Matt 11:30)

May we be inspired to move like the tribe of Issachar. Look how scripture describes them...*"Of the sons of Issachar, they were men who understood the times, with knowledge of what Israel should do..." (1 Chron 12:32).* They knew the secret in spending time in His word and gained revelation and insight on how and when to move. As they did, they gained understanding and confidence in God. We can too! All we have to do is cry out to Him. *"Call to Me and I will answer you, and I will tell you great and mighty things, which you do not know." (Jer 33:3)* He has secrets to share with us this month and He will reveal them to us... *"The secret things belong to the Lord our God, but the things revealed belong to us and to our sons forever, that we may observe all the words of this law." (Deut 29:29)* May we spend time in His word and plant His secrets, the powerful seeds of His word in our hearts. (Mk 4)

Do you find yourself in a transitional period? Are you starting to murmur? Are you having a hard time praising Him? Run into His Name! Ask Him to give you a fresh revelation of His love for you as your Healer, Banner and Provider. Are you weighed down with worries or cares? Cast them onto the Lord, your Ox, your burden-bearer. Do you want to know secrets from God Himself? Sure you do! He is ready and willing. All you have to do is get in the secret place with Him and receive a fresh revelation from His word and His great love for you! (Gal 5:6)

Journal for Iyar 5781

Use the space below to record your thoughts, praises and prayers for this month.

_____
_____
_____
_____
_____
_____
_____
_____
_____
_____
_____
_____
_____
_____
_____
_____
_____
_____
_____
_____
_____
_____
_____
_____
_____
_____
_____
_____
_____
_____
_____
_____
_____

Chalkboard Teaching for Iyar 5781

Go to "Chalkboard Teachings" page at www.christinevales.com or scan QR Code below.
Enjoy watching the chalkboard teaching for this month. Use space below to take notes.

Scan QR code to go directly to "Chalkboard Teachings" page at www.christinevales.com.

58

Prophetic Fact Sheet for Iyar 5781

BABYLONIAN NAME
IYAR
- "The Beauty of Blooming Flowers"
- Hebrew Acronym "I AM God Your Healer"
- Exo 15:26

HEBREW NAME
ZIV
- "Splendor", "Radiance"

MONTH OF THE YEAR
2nd MONTH OF SPIRITUAL YEAR
- Hebrew Letter Bet = 2
- A House, Tent, Household

8th MONTH OF PHYSICAL/CIVIL YEAR
- Hebrew Letter Chet = 8
- A Fence, Chamber, Heart, To Protect or Separate
- New Beginnings, Letter of Life

SEASON (Moed)
AVIV (Spring)	• Season of Deliverance
TRIBES of AVIV	• Yehudah, Yisachar, Zvulun

MONTHLY THEMES of AVIV
NISSAN	• Month of Redemption
IYAR	• Month of Transition
SIVAN	• Month of Extravagant Provision

APPOINTED TIMES (Moedim)
IYAR 1	✿ROSH CHODESH IYAR (Head of Month Iyar) • Ps 81:1-4
IYAR 2	✿YOM HaZICHARON (Memorial Day)
IYAR 3	✿YOM HaATZMAUT (Israel Independence Day)
IYAR 14	✿PESACH SHENI (Second Passover) • Num 9:9-12, 2 Chron 30
IYAR 28	✿YOM YERUSHALAYIM (Jerusalem Day)
NISSAN 16- SIVAN 6	✿SEFIRAT HaOMER (Counting The Omer) • 50-day countdown to Shavu'ot (Pentecost)
Date to Note... IYAR 25	✿YESHUA'S ACENSION • 40th Day of the Omer Count, Acts 1:3

COLOR/GEMSTONE
COLOR	Royal Blue
GEMSTONE	Lapis

TRIBE OF ISRAEL
YISACHAR (Issachar)
- "Adonai Brings Reward"
- 9th Son of Ya'akov
- 5th Son by Le'ah (Gen 30:17)

Ya'akov's Prophetic Blessing (Gen 49:14-15) *"Yisachar is a strong donkey, lying down between the sheepfolds. When he saw that a resting place was good and that the land was pleasant, he bowed his shoulder to bear burdens and became a slave of forced labor."*
- Camped east of tabernacle w/Yehudah & Zvulun (Num 2)
- Flag: Dark blue with sun and moon (Gen 49:14,15)
- Yisachar understands times & seasons (1 Chron 12:32)
- Scholarly tribe

HEBREW LETTER

VAV
- 6th Letter of the Hebrew Alphabet
- Numerical Value: 6
- A Tent Peg, Hook, Nail, Link, Connection, Man's Efforts
- To Link, Add, Secure, Connect
- Pesach is "Vav-ed" to Shavu'ot by Sefirat HaOmer
- "Vav" scriptures: Gen. 1:1, Exo 27:9-10, Jud 4:21

ACTION/BODY PART
INTROSPECTION	• Thought, "Counting The Omer"
RIGHT KIDNEY	• Kidneys "Give Advice" (Ps 16:7), Discernment • Right side is your spiritual side (Isa 48:13)

CONSTELLATION
SHUR or REEM (Taurus)
- Coming and Ruling Wild Ox
- Symbol of strength
- Cast your cares upon Him because He cares for you (1 Pet 5:7)
- Move from strength to strength and glory to glory (Ps 84:7)

MONTHLY CHARACTERISTICS
- Connecting month/ Abide in Him (John 15:4)
- Month Jesus walked the earth after His resurrection (Jn 20)
- Jesus delights in revealing Himself to you (Lk 24:45)
- Be reminded His presence is your most valuable asset
- Receive revelation & understand secrets (Matt 13:11)
- His Word is near you (Deut 30:14)
- "Secret" scriptures (Deut 29:29, Dan 2:21-22, Jer 33:3)
- Listen to His secrets in the stillness (Ps 46:10)
- You do not serve an "unknown god" (Jn 17:3, Acts 17:23)
- Meditate on His names revealed this month (Ex 15-17)
- Jehovah Rapha (Healer), Jireh (Provider), Nissi (Banner)
- Meditate on healing is part of your salvation (Rom 8:11)
- By His stripes we *were* healed & *are* healed (Isa 53:5, 1 Pet 2:24)
- Month manna first fell from heaven (Exo 16)
- Month Moses struck rock / Water in desert (Ex 17, 1 Cor 10:4)
- Partake of His "Superfoods"/ His Word & Spirit (Ps 78:19)
- Month Israel transitioned from Egypt to the "Midbar" (Ex 15-18)
- Hear Him in the "Midmar"- The wilderness, To speak, lead
- Receive counsel from His word (Ps 119:99, Prov 15:22)
- Consider delegating tasks to others (Ex 18)
- Take upon the secret of His light & easy yoke (Matt 11:28)
- Month Solomon began to build the temple (1 Kin 6)
- Contemplating numbers as you "Count The Omer"

Bible Study & Thought Questions
For Individual & Group Study

Dive into this portion of the New Testament for further reflection on the theme of the month. Ponder thought questions that follow and use space for personal reflection and group study.

John 6:32-40

26 Jesus answered them and said, "Truly, truly, I say to you, you seek Me, not because you saw signs, but because you ate of the loaves and were filled. **27** Do not work for the food which perishes, but for the food which endures to eternal life, which the Son of Man will give to you, for on Him the Father, God, has set His seal." **28** Therefore they said to Him, "What shall we do, so that we may work the works of God?" **29** Jesus answered and said to them, "This is the work of God, that you believe in Him whom He has sent." **30** So they said to Him, "What then do You do for a sign, so that we may see, and believe You? What work do You perform? **31** Our fathers ate the manna in the wilderness; as it is written, 'He gave them bread out of heaven to eat.'"

32 Jesus then said to them, "Truly, truly, I say to you, it is not Moses who has given you the bread out of heaven, but it is My Father who gives you the true bread out of heaven. **33** For the bread of God is that which comes down out of heaven, and gives life to the world." **34** Then they said to Him, "Lord, always give us this bread." **35** Jesus said to them, "I am the bread of life; he who comes to Me will not hunger, and he who believes in Me will never thirst. **36** But I said to you that you have seen Me, and yet do not believe. **37** All that the Father gives Me will come to Me, and the one who comes to Me I will certainly not cast out. **38** For I have come down from heaven, not to do My own will, but the will of Him who sent Me. **39** This is the will of Him who sent Me, that of all that He has given Me I lose nothing, but raise it up on the last day. **40** For this is the will of My Father, that everyone who beholds the Son and believes in Him will have eternal life, and I Myself will raise him up on the last day."

Thought Questions for Iyar 5781

What kind of bread were the disciples seeking?

_____
_____
_____
_____
_____
_____

What was the true bread Jesus was referring to and what promises did He make to those who believe?

_____
_____
_____
_____
_____
_____

How do we receive this true bread?

_____
_____
_____
_____
_____
_____

In this month where manna first fell from heaven (Ex 16), how often do you partake of the true bread from heaven? What is the difference between the manna Moses gave through God and the Bread of Life?

_____
_____
_____
_____
_____

Jesus said I AM the Bread of Life. What secrets have been revealed to you this month as you have feed on the true manna from heaven?

_____
_____
_____
_____
_____

Iyar 5781

Yom Rishon (1st Day)	Yom Sheni (2nd Day)	Yom Sh'lishi (3rd Day)	Yom Revi'i (4th Day)
Sunday	**Monday**	**Tuesday**	**Wednesday**
	NISSAN 30 APR 12 Omer 15 ◯Rosh Chodesh IYAR	1 APR 13 Omer 16 ◯Rosh Chodesh IYAR	2 APR 14 Omer 17 ✡Yom HaZicharon (Memorial Day)
6 APR 18 Omer 21	7 APR 19 Omer 22	8 APR 20 Omer 23	9 APR 21 Omer 24
13 APR 25 Omer 28	14 ●APR 26 Omer 29 ✡Pesach Sheni (Second Passover)	15 APR 27 Omer 30	16 APR 28 Omer 31
20 MAY 2 Omer 35	21 MAY 3 Omer 36	22 MAY 4 Omer 37	23 MAY 5 Omer 38
27 MAY 9 Omer 42	28 MAY 10 Omer 43 ✡Yom Yerushalayim (Jerusalem Day)	29 MAY 11 Omer 44 ◯Rosh Chodesh SIVAN	

April/May 2021

Yom Chamishi (5th Day)	Yom Shishi (6th Day)	Yom Shabbat (The Shabbat)	Moed
Thursday	**Friday**	**Saturday**	**Season**
3 APR 15 Omer 18 ✡Yom HaAtzmaut (Yisra'el Independence Day)	4 APR 16 Omer 19 🕯️ *Shabbat begins*	5 APR 17 Omer 20 🕯️ *Shabbat ends*	**Aviv (Spring)** *Season of Deliverance*
10 APR 22 Omer 25	11 APR 23 Omer 26 🕯️ *Shabbat begins*	12 APR 24 Omer 27 🕯️ *Shabbat ends*	**Months of Aviv** Nissan *Month of Redemption* Iyar *Month of Transition* Sivan *Month of Extravagant Provision*
17 APR 29 Omer 32	18 APR 30 Omer 33 🕯️ *Shabbat begins*	19 MAY 1 Omer 34 🕯️ *Shabbat ends*	**Tribes of Aviv** Yehuda *Praise of Adonai* Yisachar *Adonai Brings Reward* Zvulum *Dwelling Wished For*
24 MAY 6 Omer 39	25 MAY 7 Omer 40 ✝Yeshua's Ascension (Acts 1) 🕯️ *Shabbat begins*	26 MAY 8 Omer 41 🕯️ *Shabbat ends*	**Notes**

Bible Portions for Iyar 5781

Read through the Torah in a year and glean from the Prophets and the New Testament.
Space provided for notes.

Week of:
Iyar 5, 5781/ Apr 17, 2021

Torah Portion: **Tazria** *(She conceives)* Lev 12:1- 13:59
Prophets Portion: 2 Kings 4:42- 5:19
NT Portion: Matt 8:1- 4

Torah Portion: **Metzora** *(Leper)* Lev 14:1- 15:33
Prophets Portion: 2 Kings 7:3- 20
NT Portion: Rom 6:8- 23

_____
_____
_____
_____

Week of:
Iyar 12, 5781/ Apr 24, 2021

Torah Portion: **Acharei Mot** *(After The Death)* Lev 16:1- 18:30
Prophets Portion: Amos 9:7- 15
NT Portion: Heb 9:11- 28

Torah Portion: **Kedoshim** *(Holy Ones)* Lev 19:1- 20:27
Prophets Portion: Eze 20:2- 20, 22:1- 19
NT Portion: 1 Pet 1:13- 16

_____
_____
_____
_____

Week of:
Iyar 19, 5781/ May 1, 2021

Torah Portion: **Emor** *(Say)* Lev 21:1- 24:23
Prophets Portion: Eze 44:15- 31
NT Portion: 1 Pet 2:4- 10

_____
_____

Week of:
Iyar 26, 5781/ May 8, 2021

Torah Portion: **Behar** *(On the mountain)* Lev 25:1- 26:2
Prophets Portion: Jer 32:6- 27
NT Portion: Luke 4:16- 21

Torah Portion: **Bechukotal** *(In My statutes)* Lev 26:3- 27:34
Prophets Portion: Jer 16:19- 17:14
NT Portion: 2 Cor 6:14- 18

_____
_____
_____
_____

Sivan 5781

May 12 – June 10, 2021

Third Month of Spiritual Year
30 days

Camels on the Horizon in Sivan

Do you see camels on the horizon? That's the reality of Sivan. The third month of the Hebrew year is connected with the third Hebrew letter called "Gimel", which is a picture of a camel. Sounds funny right? However, we will soon discover camels are a perfect depiction of this month of Sivan, the month of provision.

What do you think of when you hear of "camels on the horizon?" If you lived back in Biblical times, you would rejoice if you saw camels loaded with treasures on their backs heading to your house. I guess it's our modern-day equivalent to that feeling we get when we see the UPS truck pull up to our home. There is an excitement because we are about to get something! Provision and supply are heading to our doorstep. This is what this month is all about. And guess what? These special "packages" are from the Giver of all good things, God Himself. So let's unpack this month and see what's inside!

The Lord gives many gifts all year long, but it is in Sivan when we see His extravagant gift-giving nature uniquely displayed. The Lord even has a specific day of giving in this month. What day you ask? Well, if you have been tracking with us, we have been following the Lord's instruction to count fifty days from Yeshua's resurrection. It's on this final day of the count, known as Pentecost or Shavu'ot, when His special deliveries arrive. On this fiftieth day of the count, the Lord not only gave the physical provision of the wheat harvest (Lev 23), but He also gave the spiritual provision of Himself. How so? In the Old Testament we discover He gave us Himself through His Word at Mt Sinai. (Ex 19) Fast forward to the New Testament and we learn He gave us Himself through the Holy Spirit. (Acts 2) His word and His Spirit were both given on this same exact fiftieth day. This is not a coincidence nor is it just a story of how the Lord provided for one group of people at one time in history. The Lord is truly the Gift that keeps on giving. (Eph 2:8-9) He offers these gifts of Himself to each of us afresh today!

To gain the full benefit of a gift we have to not only receive it... but actually use it! The Lord knows we are coming into a new harvest and wants us to be fruitful. The gift of His Word offers us the wisdom to move into the new with truth and love while the gift of His Spirit empowers us with supernatural strength and abilities not our own. These gifts are right on time, sitting at our doorstep with our name on them and are just waiting to be opened! Once we open and use these sacred gifts, may we be reminded of what most mothers say… "Don't forget to say 'Thank you!'" Giving thanks to the Lord is not only kind and courteous, but actually benefits us as well. Thanksgiving shows our maturity and focuses our attention back on Him, the true Gift and Source of our joy. Lastly, the gift-giving process would not be complete if we didn't share our gift with others. Ask the Lord for opportunities to share Him with others this month. He may call you to share your time or resources with another in need, for we are blessed so we can be a blessing to others. (Gen 12:2) Be sensitive to His voice and ready to saddle up on one of His camels to bring provision to others.

When we think of provision, we cannot help but think of financial provision. This is on the Lord's heart too. In fact, the tribe of this month, Zebulun, were successful businessmen. Zebulun led Israel forth in trade. They were gifted with the ability to prosper in commerce. In this "business person's month", let's review our business practices and finances and learn from Zebulun. Some of us may be considering a new job or need a fresh wind from Him over our current occupation. Be reminded, it is the Lord who gives us the power to create wealth (Deut 8:18) and He knows the plans He has for us and is good to lead us into them… all we have to do is receive. *"Let the favor of the Lord our God be upon us and confirm for us the work of our hands. Yes, confirm the work of our hands." (Ps 90:18)*

Are you feeling overwhelmed or weary? Behold! The Lord is sending camels to your door with sacred gifts of His refreshment! Open up His Word, breathe in His Spirit afresh and be revived! Are you concerned about your finances? Do you need wisdom in the work He is called you to do? Allow Him to confirm the work of your hands. Take care of any "unfinished business" in your heart. Take some time to list ways He has provided for you and thank Him. Also, consider how you can provide for others, be it with your time or money and discover that… *"It is more blessed to give than to receive." (Acts 20:35)*

Journal for Sivan 5781

Use the space below to record your thoughts, praises and prayers for this month.

Go to "Chalkboard Teachings" page at www.christinevales.com or scan QR Code below.
Enjoy watching the chalkboard teaching for this month. Use space below to take notes.

Scan QR code to go directly to "Chalkboard Teachings" page at www.christinevales.com.

68

Prophetic Fact Sheet for Sivan 5781

BABYLONIAN NAME
SIVAN •"Bright Their Covering"

HEBREW NAME
NONE

MONTH OF THE YEAR
3rd MONTH OF SPIRITUAL YEAR
- •Hebrew Letter Gimel = 3
- •A Camel, Provision, Lifted Up, Divine Fullness, Trinity

9th MONTH OF PHYSICAL/CIVIL YEAR
- •Hebrew Letter Tet = 9
- •Letter with a Choice of Life or Death:
A Basket of Fruit, Womb, Fruit of Spirit (Gal 5) **OR**
A Basket w/Twisted Snake, Surround, Finality, Judgment

SEASON (Moed)
AVIV (Spring)	•Season of Deliverance
TRIBES of AVIV	•Yehudah, Yisachar, Zvulun

MONTHLY THEMES of AVIV
NISSAN	•Month of Redemption
IYAR	•Month of Transition
SIVAN	•Month of Extravagant Provision

APPOINTED TIMES (Moedim)
SIVAN 1	✿**ROSH CHODESH SIVAN** (Head of Month, Sivan)
	•Ps 81:1-4
NISSAN 16 -SIVAN 6	✿**SEFIRAT HaOMER** (Counting The Omer)
	•50-day countdown to Shavu'ot (Pentecost)
SIVAN 6	✿**SHAVU'OT** (Feast of Weeks)
	•Exo 19 & 20 (Giving of the Torah)
	•50th Day of Counting The Omer / Pentecost
	•Acts 2 (Giving of The Holy Spirit)
	•Celebrates ingathering of the wheat harvest

COLORS / GEMSTONES
COLORS	White, Clear
GEMSTONES	White Moonstone, Clear Quartz

TRIBE OF ISRAEL
ZVULUN (Zebulun) •"Dwelling Wished For"
- •10th Son of Ya'akov
- •6th Son by Le'ah (Gen 30:19-20)

• **Ya'akov's Prophetic Blessing** (Gen 49:13) *"Zvulun will dwell at the seashore and he shall be a haven for ships and his flank shall be toward Sidon."*

- •Camped east of tabernacle w/Yehudah & Yisachar (Num 2)
- •Flag: White with a Ship (Gen 49:13)
- •Tribe of "businessmen"
- •Supported Torah study of brothers in the tribe of Yisachar

HEBREW LETTER

ZAYIN
- •7th Letter of the Hebrew Alphabet
- •Numerical Value: 7
- •Perfection, Completion, Rest
- •A Plough, Sword, Weapon
- •To Cut Off, Nourish, Feed
- •All 7's are important and dear to The Lord

ACTION/BODY PART
WALKING	•Continual ongoing progress (Jn 8:31, 2 Jn 1:6)
	•Jesus said "Follow Me" (Matt 4:19)
LEFT FOOT	•Walking with security (Prov 10:9)
	•Left side is your physical side (Isa 48:13)

CONSTELLATION
THAUMIM (Gemini)
- •The Twins
- •Rebecca birthed twins, Esau and Jacob, in Sivan
- •"Twin Tablets" of His Word given at Mt Sinai in Sivan

MONTHLY CHARACTERISTICS
- •Receive and rest in His extravagant provision
- •Month celebrating the giving of His Word (Exo 19 & 20)
- •The letter kills, the Spirit gives life & freedom (2 Cor 3)
- •Receive fresh revelation from His Word (Mat 4:4, Jn 6:63)
- •Month when Holy Spirit was given to believers (Acts 2)
- •Don't go any further in your own strength (Acts 1:4-8)
- •Receive baptism of Holy Spirit (Acts 2)
- •Empowered by His Spirit to do even greater works (Jn 14:12)
- •Pray in the Spirit/ Speak His Word w/boldness (Acts 2-4)
- •Exit the wilderness empowered in the Holy Spirit (Lk 4:14)
- •Enlarge boundaries & place of your tent, like Zvulun (Isa 54:2)
- •Created in His image as extravagant givers (Jn 3:16)
- •Let joy be your "barometer" in giving (2 Cor 9:7, 2 Chron 31)
- •Our covenant in Him: Blessed to be a blessing (Gen 12:2)
- •Enough & Extra, Bread & Seed (Matt 14:17-21, 2 Cor 9:10)
- •The "Business Person's Month" (Zvulun)
- •Ask the Lord bless & confirm work of your hands (Ps 90:17)
- •Given power to create wealth (Deut 8:18, Isa 48:15-17)
- •Read New Testament definition of prosperity (2 Cor 9:8)
- •Receive His mercies & grace to complete assignments
- •Consider timely reading of Ruth (Barley to wheat harvest)
- •Walk circumspectly, in love & by the Spirit (Gal 5, Eph 5)
- •Consider your inheritance wisely, Jacob & Esau (Gen 25:19-34)

Sivan 5781
Bible Study & Thought Questions
For Individual & Group Study

Dive into this portion of the New Testament for further reflection on the theme of the month. Ponder thought questions that follow and use space for personal reflection and group study.

Matthew 14:15-21

15 When it was evening, the disciples came to Him and said, "This place is desolate and the hour is already late; so send the crowds away, that they may go into the villages and buy food for themselves." **16** But Jesus said to them, "They do not need to go away; you give them something to eat!" **17** They said to Him, "We have here only five loaves and two fish." **18** And He said, "Bring them here to Me." **19** Ordering the people to sit down on the grass, He took the five loaves and the two fish, and looking up toward heaven, He blessed the food, and breaking the loaves He gave them to the disciples, and the disciples gave them to the crowds, **20** and they all ate and were satisfied. They picked up what was left over of the broken pieces, twelve full baskets. **21** There were about five thousand men who ate, besides women and children.

2 Corinthians 9:6-15

6 Now this I say, he who sows sparingly will also reap sparingly, and he who sows bountifully will also reap bountifully. **7** Each one must do just as he has purposed in his heart, not grudgingly or under compulsion, for God loves a cheerful giver. **8** And God is able to make all grace abound to you, so that always having all sufficiency in everything, you may have an abundance for every good deed; **9** as it is written, "He scattered abroad, he gave to the poor, His righteousness endures forever." **10** Now He who supplies seed to the sower and bread for food will supply and multiply your seed for sowing and increase the harvest of your righteousness; **11** you will be enriched in everything for all liberality, which through us is producing thanksgiving to God. **12** For the ministry of this service is not only fully supplying the needs of the saints, but is also overflowing through many thanksgivings to God. **13** Because of the proof given by this ministry, they will glorify God for your obedience to your confession of the gospel of Christ and for the liberality of your contribution to them and to all, **14** while they also, by prayer on your behalf, yearn for you because of the surpassing grace of God in you. **15** Thanks be to God for His indescribable gift!

Thought Questions for Sivan 5781

Before Jesus fed the multitude, He first told His disciples, "You should give them something to eat." How did Jesus demonstrate His Father's power and will for His disciples?

_____
_____
_____
_____
_____

What did Jesus do with the food that was given to him? What happened next?

_____
_____
_____
_____
_____

In this month of provision, after meditating on Jesus' example in Matthew 14- what are you doing with what seems like "not enough"? Are you cursing it or blessing it? What can you expect from your actions?

_____
_____
_____
_____
_____

After meditating on 2 Corinthians, how has the Holy Spirit encouraged you through His promise to provide seed to the sower and bread for food? (v 10) What is your response?

_____
_____
_____
_____
_____

The Lord loves a cheerful giver. If He can get it through you- He will get it to you. What area of giving has the Lord prompted you to give?

_____
_____
_____
_____

Sivan 5781

Yom Rishon (1st Day)	Yom Sheni (2nd Day)	Yom Sh'lishi (3rd Day)	Yom Revi'i (4th Day)
Sunday	**Monday**	**Tuesday**	**Wednesday**
		IYAR 29 MAY 11 Omer 44 ◯Rosh Chodesh SIVAN	**1** MAY 12 Omer 45 ◯Rosh Chodesh SIVAN
5 MAY 16 Omer 49	**6** MAY 17 ✡Sefirat HaOmer Omer 50 (Counting The Omer: Nissan 16 - Sivan 6) ✡Shavu'ot (Feast of Weeks)	**7** MAY 18	**8** MAY 19
12 MAY 23 ✝Pentecost (Christian Date Celebrating the Giving of the Holy Spirit)	**13** MAY 24	**14** MAY 25	**15** ●MAY 26
19 MAY 30	**20** MAY 31	**21** JUNE 1	**22** JUNE 2
26 JUNE 6	**27** JUNE 7	**28** JUNE 8	**29** JUNE 9

May/June 2021

Yom Chamishi (5th Day)	Yom Shishi (6th Day)	Yom Shabbat (The Shabbat)	Moed
Thursday	**Friday**	**Saturday**	**Season**
2 MAY 13 Omer 46	3 MAY 14 Omer 47 *Shabbat begins*	4 MAY 15 Omer 48 *Shabbat ends*	**Aviv (Spring)** *Season of Deliverance*
9 MAY 20	10 MAY 21 *Shabbat begins*	11 MAY 22 *Shabbat ends*	**Months of Aviv** Nissan *Month of Redemption* Iyar *Month of Transition* Sivan *Month of Extravagant Provision*
16 MAY 27	17 MAY 28 *Shabbat begins*	18 MAY 29 *Shabbat ends*	**Tribes of Aviv** Yehuda *Praise of Adonai* Yisachar *Adonai Brings Reward* Zvulum *Dwelling Wished For*
23 JUNE 3	24 JUNE 4 *Shabbat begins*	25 JUNE 5 *Shabbat ends*	**Notes**
30 JUNE 10 ○ Rosh Chodesh TAMMUZ			

Bible Portions for Sivan 5781

Read through the Torah in a year and glean from the Prophets and the New Testament.
Space provided for notes.

Week of:
Sivan 4, 5781/ May 15, 2021

Torah Portion: **Bamidbar** *(In the desert)* Num 1:1- 4:20
Prophets Portion: Hosea 2:1- 22
NT Portion: 1 Cor 12:12- 20

_____
_____
_____
_____
_____
_____

Week of:
Sivan 11, 5781/ June 22, 2021

Torah Portion: **Nasso** *(Lift Up)* Num 4:21- 7:89
Prophets Portion: Judg 13:2- 25
NT Portion: Acts 21:17- 26

_____
_____
_____
_____
_____
_____

Week of:
Sivan 18, 5781/ June 29, 2021

Torah Portion: **Beha'alotcha** *(When you set up)* Num 8:1-12:16
Prophets Portion: Zech 2:10- 4:7
NT Portion: 1 Cor 10:6- 13

_____
_____
_____
_____
_____
_____

Week of:
Sivan 25, 5781/ June 5, 2021

Torah Portion: **Shelach** *(Send for yourself)* Num 13:1- 15:41
Prophets Portion: Josh 2:1- 24
NT Portion: Heb 3:7- 19

_____
_____
_____
_____
_____
_____

Tammuz 5781

June 11 – July 9, 2021

Fourth Month of Spiritual Year
29 days

Hidden Vision in Tammuz

Welcome to Tammuz! This fourth month of the Hebrew year, depicts a door, which swings wide into a favorite season by many... the season of summer! Summer or "kaitz" in Hebrew is often referred to as the "holiday of the eyes." We will see how this expression depicts this month as we cross over its threshold.

Everywhere we look this month, we see the Lord focusing on our vision. Why is He so adamant about where we put our eyes? *"The eye is the lamp of the body, so then if your eye is clear, your whole body will be full of light. But if your eye is bad, your whole body will be full of darkness." (Matt 6:22-23)* He knows our gaze will either lead to worship or idolatry. It was in Tammuz when Israel lost their patience and focus while waiting for Moses to return from Mt Sinai and subsequently made the infamous golden calf. (Exo 32) They sought immediate comfort and took their eyes off the Lord. When Moses returned, he could not believe *his eyes*. He smashed the tablets and destroyed the golden calf. Quick fixes and idols in our lives enslave us. Once idols are exposed and destroyed we can redirect our eyes and heart to worship the One, True and Living God.

So how do we guard these eyes of ours that often get us into a lot of trouble? It actually starts in our hearts, *"Above all else, guard your heart, for everything you do flows from it." (Prov 4:23)* Our eyes take in things and deposit them into our heart. All the issues of our lives flow from our heart. When we seek His help to guard or *"hide"* our eyes in this *"hidden"* month of Tammuz, we actually guard our heart. *"For where your treasure is, there your heart will be also." (Matt 6:21)*

The Lord calls us to fix our eyes on the unseen or hidden things. One definition of the word Tammuz is "hidden." *"So we fix our eyes not on what is seen, but on what is unseen, since what is seen is temporary, but what is unseen is eternal."(2 Cor 4:18)* Jesus said... *"Blessed are they who did not see, and yet believed." (John 20:29)* How do we see hidden things? His Word tells us when we turn to the Lord, the "veil" is removed from our eyes - from our heart. (2 Cor 3:16) As we turn our eyes to Jesus, He enables us to "see" things we could never see with our natural eyes. He opens the eyes of the blind. (Ps 146:8) His perfect Light exposes hidden things in our lives that we "just don't see." When He reveals... He heals. He is better than any eye doctor I know! (Eph 1:18)

Looking to the heavens this month we see the constellation, Cancer. Cancer or "Sartan" in Hebrew means "filmstrip." Thus, Tammuz is often referred to as "The Filmstrip Month." Sartan also means "to remove the mud." I can't help but think of when you remove a pair of eyeglasses to clean them and suddenly realize how dirty they were. You thought you were seeing clearly, but when you take time to wipe them off, you see better than before! Let us take time this month to stop and look at our life, frame by frame, holding up each section of our lives to the light of His Truth and allow Him to bring clarity so we can make adjustments. The Lord highlights our right hand and it's index finger, which is actually connected with our vision. How so? When we point our finger at something, we are directing one's attention and focus in that direction. The Jews have a beautiful wedding tradition underscoring this point. The bride wears her wedding band on her right index finger which directs her gaze to her bridegroom. How much more does The Bride of Christ need that reminder... to fix her gaze on her heavenly Bridegroom, Yeshua.

Tammuz also means "to connect." This is a time where He brings us from one large expanse into another. He does this by taking us through a narrow, protective place. A connection to consider this month is the Biblical three-week "connecting" period called "Between The Straits." This place of the straits is not a place where God withholds things from us, but is a place where He reminds us of our greatest asset, His presence. May our hands be raised in worship and eyes fixed on Him as we move through the straits, for it is a protected transforming passage of time that will bless us if we have eyes to see and ears to hear. *"For the gate is small and the way is narrow that leads to life, and there are few who find it." (Matt 7:14)*

So where is your gaze? Are you using your spiritual eyes or natural ones? Are you beholding Him or have you grown impatient and turned to a golden calf? Ask Him to reveal any idols you may have erected in your life. How can you practically guard your heart? Ask Him to give you His eyes to see the unseen. Look closely at your connections this month and prayerfully consider your handshakes. Be aware of this divine connecting time "Between the Straits" and may your eyes ever be upon Him. *(Ps 25:15)*

Journal for Tammuz 5781

Use the space below to record your thoughts, praises and prayers for this month.

_____

_____

_____

_____

_____

_____

_____

_____

_____

_____

_____

_____

_____

_____

_____

_____

_____

_____

_____

_____

_____

_____

_____

_____

_____

_____

_____

_____

_____

_____

_____

_____

_____

Chalkboard Teaching for Tammuz 5781

Go to "Chalkboard Teachings" page at www.christinevales.com or scan QR Code below.
Enjoy watching the chalkboard teaching for this month. Use space below to take notes.

Scan QR code to go directly to "Chalkboard Teachings" page at www.christinevales.com.

78

Prophetic Fact Sheet for Tammuz 5781

BABYLONIAN NAME
TAMMUZ
- "Hidden"
- From Hebrew "Tam"= To Connect, Consummate

HEBREW NAME
NONE

MONTH OF THE YEAR
4th MONTH OF SPIRITUAL YEAR
- Hebrew Letter Dalet = 4
- A Door, Path, The Way of Life, Creativity

10th MONTH OF PHYSICAL/CIVIL YEAR
- Hebrew Letter: Yod = 10
- A Closed Hand, Mercy from The Hand of God
- An Action, Work
- Humility, Holiness, Perfection, Godly Authority
- Number of Order, Tithe and Testimony

SEASON (Moed)
KAITZ (Summer)
- Season of Preparation

TRIBES of KAITZ
- Reuven, Shimon, Gad

MONTHLY THEMES of KAITZ
TAMMUZ	• Guarding Our Heart & Eyes
AV	• Believing Abba
ELUL	• The King is in The Field

APPOINTED TIMES (Moedim)
TAMMUZ 1
- ✿ROSH CHODESH TAMMUZ (Head of Month Tammuz)
- Ps 81:1-4

TAMMUZ 9
- ✿TISHA B' TAMMUZ (Ninth of Tammuz)
- Fast commemorates Nebuchadnezzar's first breach of the walls of Jerusalem
- 2 Kings 25:2-7

  *NOTE…Tisha B'Tammuz in Recent History:
- Tammuz 9, 5775 (June 26, 2015)
- America struck down God's definition of marriage

TAMMUZ 17
- ✿TZOM TAMMUZ (Fast of Tammuz)
- Sin of idolatry of the golden calf
- Moses smashed first set of tablets
- Exo 32

TAMMUZ 18 -AV 9
- ✿BEIN HaMETZARIM (Between The Straits)
- "Between The Months" of Tammuz and Av
- Dates book-end two events in Israel's history: Day Moses came down w/ first set of Ten Commandments & Day spies returned from surveying promised land.
- Num 13, Lam 1:3, Prov 4:20-27

COLOR/GEMSTONE
| COLOR | Red |
| GEMSTONE | Carnelian |

TRIBE OF ISRAEL
REUVEN (Reuben)
- "Behold A Son"
- Firstborn of Ya'akov
- 1st Son by Le'ah (Gen 29:32)

• **Ya'akov's Prophetic Blessing** (Gen 49:3-4) *"Reuven, you are my firstborn. My might and the beginning of my strength. Preeminent in dignity and preeminent in power. Uncontrolled as water, you shall not have preeminence, because you went up to your father's bed, then you defiled it, he went up to my couch."*
- Camped south of tabernacle w/Shimon & Gad (Num 2)
- Flag: Red with mandrakes (Gen 30:14)
- Reuven lost his inheritance, but his life was redeemed
- Gen 35:27, Deut 33:6

HEBREW LETTER

CHET
- 8th Letter of the Hebrew Alphabet
- Numerical Value: 8
- New Beginnings, Doorway, Fence, Threshold
- Private Chamber, Heart, Separate, Inner Room
- Letter of Life, Grace, Wisdom, Light radiating from eyes
- Formed from Vav & Zayin, letters of previous months

ACTION/BODY PART
SIGHT
- Guard eyes, Kaitz = "Holiday of the Eyes"

RIGHT HAND & IT'S FINGER
- Index finger, directing one's sight
- Right side is your spiritual side (Isa 48:13)
- Hebrew brides wore ring on right index finger directing her gaze to her Bridegroom (SOS 1:15)
- "Yad"= Torah pointer designed w/ index finger at its tip, directing eyes and heart of the reader

CONSTELLATION
SARTAN (Cancer)
- The Crab
- One who holds or binds
- Keep heart soft and vulnerable to the Lord (Eze 36:26)
- Don't harden your heart to the Lord (Heb 3:15)
- Harden your heart toward the enemy (Js 4:7)

MONTHLY CHARACTERISTICS
- Guard your heart by guarding your eyes (Prov 4:23)
- Don't lose your focus/ Keep your eyes on Jesus (Heb 12:2)
- Magnify the Lord, not your circumstances (Ps 34:3)
- See things from your seat in heavenly places (Eph 1)
- Month Moses came down Mt Sinai w/ first set of tablets
- Choose to worship the Lord and not a "golden calf"
- Tap into the patience & self-control in your Spirit (Gal 5)
- Choose patience over haste/ Declare "I have patience"
- "Filmstrip" month/ Review & adjust "frame by frame"
- Receive clarity of vision as you "look and look again"
- Write the vision, make it clear & run w/ it (Hab 2:2)
- "Watch" and consider your handshakes & covenants
- Month spies sent to survey the Promised Land (Num 13)
- Don't speak or receive evil reports/ Speak life (Prov 18:21)
- Use provision He gives for His vision for your life (2 Cor 9:8)
- "Between The Straits" begins (Tammuz 18- Av 9)
- Protected by His straits/Keep eyes on Him (Prov 4:20-27)

Tammuz 5781
<u>Bible Study & Thought Questions</u>
For Individual & Group Study

Dive into this portion of the New Testament for further reflection on the theme of the month. Ponder thought questions that follow and use space for personal reflection and group study.

Matthew 6:22-23

22 "The eye is the lamp of the body; so then if your eye is clear, your whole body will be full of light. 23 But if your eye is bad, your whole body will be full of darkness. If then the light that is in you is darkness, how great is the darkness!

2 Corinthians 4:16-18

16 Therefore we do not lose heart, but though our outer man is decaying, yet our inner man is being renewed day by day. 17 For momentary, light affliction is producing for us an eternal weight of glory far beyond all comparison, 18 while we look not at the things which are seen, but at the things which are not seen; for the things which are seen are temporal, but the things which are not seen are eternal.

Ephesians 1:15-23

15 For this reason I too, having heard of the faith in the Lord Jesus which exists among you and your love for all the saints, 16 do not cease giving thanks for you, while making mention of you in my prayers; 17 that the God of our Lord Jesus Christ, the Father of glory, may give to you a spirit of wisdom and of revelation in the knowledge of Him. 18 I pray that the eyes of your heart may be enlightened, so that you will know what is the hope of His calling, what are the riches of the glory of His inheritance in the saints, 19 and what is the surpassing greatness of His power toward us who believe. These are in accordance with the working of the strength of His might 20 which He brought about in Christ, when He raised Him from the dead and seated Him at His right hand in the heavenly places, 21 far above all rule and authority and power and dominion, and every name that is named, not only in this age but also in the one to come. 22 And He put all things in subjection under His feet, and gave Him as head over all things to the church, 23 which is His body, the fullness of Him who fills all in all.

Thought Questions for Tammuz 5781

After meditating on the verses in Matthew, how are your eyes like a lamp?

_____
_____
_____
_____
_____
_____

2 Corinthians 4:16 tells us our inner man is being renewed day by day. In what ways can we nourish our soul?

_____
_____
_____
_____
_____
_____

Ephesians 1 says the eyes of our heart can be enlightened. How does this occur? See Psalm 146:8. In verses 18 & 19, name the three things Paul wants these believers to know.

_____
_____
_____
_____
_____

How has the Holy Spirit encouraged you in this month of vision?

_____
_____
_____
_____
_____

Where is your gaze? What things are in the forefront? In what areas is He calling you to refocus? See Psalm 101:3 for encouragement.

_____
_____
_____
_____
_____

Tammuz 5781

Yom Rishon (1st Day)	Yom Sheni (2nd Day)	Yom Sh'lishi (3rd Day)	Yom Revi'i (4th Day)
Sunday	**Monday**	**Tuesday**	**Wednesday**
3 JUNE 13	4 JUNE 14	5 JUNE 15	6 JUNE 16
10 JUNE 20 ✡Tisha B'Tammuz (Fast Commemorating Nebuchadnezzar's First Breach of The Walls of Jerusalem - Tammuz 9)	11 JUNE 21	12 JUNE 22	13 JUNE 23
17 JUNE 27 ✡Tzom Tammuz (Fast of Tammuz)	18 JUNE 28 ✡Bein HaMetzarim (Between The Straits, Day 1/21) (Tammuz 18 - Av 9)	19 JUNE 29 ✡Bein HaMetzarim (Between The Straits, Day 2/21)	20 JUNE 30 ✡Bein HaMetzarim (Between The Straits, Day 3/21)
24 JULY 4 ✡Bein HaMetzarim (Between The Straits, Day 7/21)	25 JULY 5 ✡Bein HaMetzarim (Between The Straits, Day 8/21)	26 JULY 6 ✡Bein HaMetzarim (Between The Straits, Day 9/21)	27 JULY 7 ✡Bein HaMetzarim (Between The Straits, Day 10/21)

June/July 2021

Yom Chamishi (5th Day)	Yom Shishi (6th Day)	Yom Shabbat (The Shabbat)	Moed
Thursday	**Friday**	**Saturday**	**Season**
SIVAN 30　　JUNE 10 ○Rosh Chodesh TAMMUZ	**1**　　JUNE 11 ○Rosh Chodesh TAMMUZ 🕯🕯 *Shabbat begins*	**2**　　JUNE 12 🕯 *Shabbat ends*	**Kaitz (Summer)** *Season of Preparation*
7　　JUNE 17	**8**　　JUNE 18 🕯🕯 *Shabbat begins*	**9**　　JUNE 19 🕯 *Shabbat ends*	**Months of Kaitz** Tammuz *Guarding Our Heart & Eyes* Av *Believing The Father's Goodness* Elul *The King is in The Field*
14　●JUNE 24	**15**　　JUNE 25 🕯🕯 *Shabbat begins*	**16**　　JUNE 26 🕯 *Shabbat ends*	**Tribes of Kaitz** Reuven *Behold, A Son* Shimon *Gracious Hearing* Gad *A Troop, Good Fortune*
21　　JULY 1 ✡Bein HaMetzarim (Between The Straits, Day 4/21)	**22**　　JULY 2 ✡Bein HaMetzarim (Between The Straits, Day 5/21) 🕯🕯 *Shabbat begins*	**23**　　JULY 3 ✡Bein HaMetzarim (Between The Straits, Day 6/21) 🕯 *Shabbat ends*	**Notes**
28　　JULY 8 ✡Bein HaMetzarim (Between The Straits, Day 11/21)	**29**　　JULY 9 ✡Bein HaMetzarim (Between The Straits, Day 12/21) ○Rosh Chodesh AV 🕯🕯*Shabbat begins*		

Bible Portions for Tammuz 5781

Read through the Torah in a year and glean from the Prophets and the New Testament.
Space provided for notes.

Week of:
Tammuz 2, 5781/ June 12, 2021

Torah Portion:
Prophets Portion:
NT Portion:

Korach *(Korah)* Num 16:1- 18:32
1 Sam 11:14- 12:22
Rom 13:1- 7

_____
_____
_____
_____
_____
_____

Week of:
Tammuz 9, 5781/ June 19, 2021

Torah Portion:
Prophets Portion:
NT Portion:

Chukat *(Decree of)* Num 19:1- 22:1
Judg 11:1- 33
John 3:10- 21

_____
_____
_____
_____
_____
_____

Week of:
Tammuz 16, 5781/ June 26, 2021

Torah Portion:
Prophets Portion:
NT Portion:

Balak *(Devastator)* Num 22:2- 25:9
Micah 5:6- 6:8
1 Cor 1:20- 31

_____
_____
_____
_____
_____
_____

Week of:
Tammuz 23, 5781/ July 3, 2021

Torah Portion:
Prophets Portion:
NT Portion:

Pinchas *(Phineahs)* Num 25:10- 29:40
1 Kings 18:46- 19:21
John 2:13- 22

_____
_____
_____
_____
_____

July 10 – August 8, 2021

Fifth Month of Spiritual Year
30 days

Choose Abba in Av

Decisions, decisions, decisions. Life is full of decisions. We make a series of choices every day of our lives. The Lord is always ready to give us His discernment. This is especially good considering all the choices we make. Such is this month of Av. As the fifth month of the year, it is associated with grace. In addition to grace we need discernment... but how do we get it? The answer lies right before our eyes. The answer is in "Av" itself.

The word Av means Abba or Father in Hebrew and is often an affectionate term like Daddy or Papa. He is the source of our discernment and very life. Question is... do we really know God as our Abba Father? We have to start here. Do we know Him as Abba? And if not, how can we? We can know Him as Abba by choosing Him. He has given us free will to make this the most important decision of all. Scripture points our hearts in the right direction- His love... *"But as many as received Him, to them He gave the right to become children of God, even to those who believe in His name, who were born, not of blood nor of the will of the flesh nor of the will of man, but of God." (Jn 1:12-13)*

Knowing Him as Abba starts with receiving His Son as Lord and Savior of our lives. Jesus said, *"If you have seen me you have seen the Father." (Jn 14:9)* When we receive Jesus, we become a new creation in Christ and a child of Abba Father. *"For all who are being led by the Spirit of God, these are sons of God. For you have not received a spirit of slavery leading to fear again, but you have received a spirit of adoption as sons by which we cry out, "Abba! Father!" (Rom 8:14)*

Hearing is the action associated with this month. *"So faith comes by comes by hearing, and hearing by the word of God." (Rom 10:17)* The word says our faith grows as we discern. Can you see how belief is linked with spiritual hearing? When God is our Abba, we have access to His discernment and wisdom. All we have to do is ask and listen as He will freely give it to us. *"But if any of you lacks wisdom, let him ask of God, who gives to all generously and without reproach, and it will be given to him." (Js 1:5)* When we position our hearts to listen and declare His word, we grow in discernment. Hearing is clearly depicted in many of this month's characteristics. The tribe associated with this month is Simeon. His name means "gracious hearing." If you study Simeon, he seems to be hard of hearing. However, he's an example of God's love and how He redeems our bad decisions as look and listen to Him. Our kidneys are highlighted this month and are known as the "advisors of the soul." How is this connected to hearing? The function of the kidneys is to purify our blood and remove toxins. They are a physical picture of discernment... a filter to purify our minds and remove bad toxins from our thoughts. We are truly fearfully and wonderfully made.

Consider how Israel was positioned in Av. Were they presented with important, life changing decisions? Yes! On the 9th of Av the spies returned with their news report of the Promised Land. (Num 13) Although there were giants in the land, Joshua and Caleb believed the Lord and encouraged Israel to possess the land. The other spies, however, gave a negative report and instilled fear. Israel was faced with choice and they went with the majority and chose unbelief. This led to devastating immediate ramifications in their history. Specifically, forty years wandering in the wilderness, culminating in the death of that entire generation twenty years and older. That generation would never enter the Promised Land.

The Lord presents us with a similar choice this month. As we come out of the three-week period called "Between the Straits" on Av 9, we stand at the edge of our promised land. As we exit this narrow passage of time, we will be presented with a choice: To believe the good report of the Lord or to settle in unbelief. Whose report will you listen to? Learn from Israel's history. Do not limit God. Choose to believe the truth of Abba's word. (Ps 78:41) If you listen closely, you will hear His voice in the stars this month as Leo, The Lion of Judah. He roars over our heads, lovingly protecting His cubs. May we recognize His roar, faithfully guiding us His way, to obtain His promises!

Where do you find yourself this month? This isn't just about Israel's history... it's about you! What choice lies before you? Whose voice will you listen to? Position yourself to hear His truth. I implore you to believe the good report of the Lord. Unbelief has severe consequences. Believing is credited to you as righteousness. (Gen 15:6) Have you accepted His offer of forgiveness and adoption? In this month of choices, make the best decision of your life. Choose this day whom you will serve... Him! (Jos 24:15)

Journal for Av 5781

Use the space below to record your thoughts, praises and prayers for this month.

_____
_____
_____
_____
_____
_____
_____
_____
_____
_____
_____
_____
_____
_____
_____
_____
_____
_____
_____
_____
_____
_____
_____
_____
_____
_____
_____
_____
_____
_____
_____
_____
_____
_____

Chalkboard Teaching for Av 5781

Go to "Chalkboard Teachings" page at www.christinevales.com or scan QR Code below.
Enjoy watching the chalkboard teaching for this month. Use space below to take notes.

Scan QR code to go directly to "Chalkboard Teachings" page at www.christinevales.com.

88

Prophetic Fact Sheet for Av 5781

BABYLONIAN NAME
AV
- "Father", "To Will or Desire"
- From Hebrew "Abba"= Father

HEBREW NAME
NONE

MONTH OF THE YEAR
5th MONTH OF SPIRITUAL YEAR
- Hebrew Letter Hei = 5
- Wind, Breath, Window, Lattice, Grace, Praise
- Behold, The One revealed

11th MONTH OF PHYSICAL/CIVIL YEAR
- Hebrew Letters Yod and Aleph = 11
- Disorder, Imperfection, Incompleteness, Unfulfillment

SEASON (Moed)
KAITZ (Summer) • Season of Preparation

TRIBES of KAITZ • Reuven, Shimon, Gad

MONTHLY THEMES of KAITZ
TAMMUZ	• Guarding Our Heart & Eyes
AV	• Believing Abba
ELUL	• The King is in The Field

APPOINTED TIMES (Moedim)
AV 1
- ✿ROSH CHODESH AV (Head of Month, Av)
- Ps 81:1-4

TAMMUZ 18-AV 9
- ✿BEIN HaMETZARIM (Between The Straits)
- "Between The Months" of Tammuz and Av
- Spies returned from surveying Promised Land
- Israel committed sin of unbelief (See TISHA B'AV)
- Num 13 & 14, Lam 1:3

AV 9
- ✿TISHA B'AV (Ninth of Av)
- Intended to be a day of celebration, believing the good report of the Lord and advancing into the Promised Land (Ps 78)
- Israel settled in the sin of unbelief and believed negative report of spies (Num 13 & 14)
- Fasting Day

NOTE...Tisha B'Av's in History:
587 BC	Babylon Destroyed Solomon's Temple
70 AD	Rome Destroyed 2nd Temple
135 AD	Final Defeat of the Jews by Rome
1095 AD	1st Crusade killing thousands of Jews
1290 AD	Jews Expelled from England
1492 AD	Jews Expelled from Spain
1942 AD	Jews Warsaw ghetto into death camps
2005 AD	Expulsion of Jews from Gaza began

AV 15
- ✿TU B'AV (Fifteenth of Av)
- Holiday of Love & Romance
- Day to celebrate the love of Abba Father

COLOR/GEMSTONE
COLOR	Green
GEMSTONE	Emerald

TRIBE OF ISRAEL
SHIMON (Simeon)
- "Gracious Hearing"
- 2nd Son of Ya'akov
- 2nd Son by Le'ah (Gen 29:33)

• **Ya'akov's Prophetic Blessing** (Gen 49:5-7) *"Simeon and Levi are brothers. Their swords are implements of violence. Let my soul not enter into their council. Let not my glory be united with their assembly because in their anger they slew men and in their self-will they lamed oxen. Cursed be their anger, for it is fierce and their wrath, for it is cruel. I will disperse them in Ya'akov and scatter them in Israel."*
- Camped south of tabernacle w/Reuven & Gad (Num 2)
- Flag: Green with city of Shechem (Gen 34)

HEBREW LETTER

TET
- 9th Letter of the Hebrew Alphabet
- Numerical Value: 9
- Letter with a Choice of Life or Death:
A Basket of Fruit, Womb, Fruit of Spirit (Gal 5) **OR**
A Basket w/Twisted Snake, Finality, Judgment, To Surround
- Choose this day whom you will serve (Josh 24:15)
- Choose Him, Choose Life (Deut 30:19, Jn 1:12)

ACTION/BODY PART
HEARING
- Hebrew "Shema"= To Understand, hear and act
- Discern truth from false (Job 12:22, Deut 6:4-9)
- 'The ear tests words as the palate tastes food' (Job 34:3)

LEFT KIDNEY
- Filters the blood
- "Advisors to the soul" (Ps 16:7)
- Spiritual Filtration System = Our Discernment
- Left side is your physical side (Isa 48:13)

CONSTELLATION
ARIEH (Leo)
- The Lion Hunting Down His Prey
- Yeshua is The Lion of the tribe of Yehudah
- Our Abba Father roars over us His cubs
- Enemy is not a lion at all, he's a LI-AR (1 Pet 5:8-9)

MONTHLY CHARACTERISTICS
- Month intended for Israel to enter the Promised Land
- Don't settle in unbelief, Unbelief limits God (Ps 78:41, Mk 6:5-6)
- Listen and believe Abba's good report and advance
- Believe His promise and mix it with faith (Heb 4:2)
- Guard your heart by guarding your hearing (Prov 4:23)
- Consider what you hear/ Listen to like-minded sources
- Faith comes by hearing & hearing by the Word of God (Rom 10:17)
- Be hearers and doers of the Word (Js 1:22-25)
- Create an environment to hear God (Jn 10:27)
- Choose to believe Him as your Abba Father (Rom 8:15)
- As a "believer" in Christ... Believe Him!
- "Take Heed" Listen to your Father before making a decision
- Protected in "The Straits"/Keep eyes on Him (Prov 4:20-27)
- "Between The Straits" ends (Tammuz 18 -Av 9)
- "Low" point on Hebrew calendar (Av 9) Israel's unbelief
- "High" point on Hebrew calendar (Av 15) Abba's Love
- Meditate upon Abba's love for you (1 Jn 4:18, Gal 5:6)

Av 5781
Bible Study & Thought Questions
For Individual & Group Study

Dive into this portion of the New Testament for further reflection on the theme of the month. Ponder thought questions that follow and use space for personal reflection and group study.

Mark 9:1-8

And Jesus was saying to them, "Truly I say to you, there are some of those who are standing here who will not taste death until they see the kingdom of God after it has come with power." [2] Six days later, Jesus took with Him Peter and James and John, and brought them up on a high mountain by themselves. And He was transfigured before them; [3] and His garments became radiant and exceedingly white, as no launderer on earth can whiten them. [4] Elijah appeared to them along with Moses; and they were talking with Jesus. [5] Peter said to Jesus, "Rabbi, it is good for us to be here; let us make three tabernacles, one for You, and one for Moses, and one for Elijah." [6] For he did not know what to answer; for they became terrified. [7] Then a cloud formed, overshadowing them, and a voice came out of the cloud, "This is My beloved Son, listen to Him!" [8] All at once they looked around and saw no one with them anymore, except Jesus alone.

John 2:1-11

On the third day there was a wedding in Cana of Galilee, and the mother of Jesus was there; [2] and both Jesus and His disciples were invited to the wedding. [3] When the wine ran out, the mother of Jesus said to Him, "They have no wine." [4] And Jesus said to her, "Woman, what does that have to do with us? My hour has not yet come." [5] His mother said to the servants, "Whatever He says to you, do it." [6] Now there were six stone waterpots set there for the Jewish custom of purification, containing twenty or thirty gallons each. [7] Jesus said to them, "Fill the waterpots with water." So they filled them up to the brim. [8] And He said to them, "Draw some out now and take it to the headwaiter." So they took it to him. [9] When the headwaiter tasted the water which had become wine, and did not know where it came from (but the servants who had drawn the water knew), the headwaiter called the bridegroom, [10] and said to him, "Every man serves the good wine first, and when the people have drunk freely, then he serves the poorer wine; but you have kept the good wine until now." [11] This beginning of His signs Jesus did in Cana of Galilee, and manifested His glory, and His disciples believed in Him.

Thought Questions for Av 5781

What did the voice from heaven instruct the disciples to do? Whose voice was this?

_____
_____
_____
_____
_____
_____

In this month of choosing to believe the Father- what choices are before you? How can we discern His voice?

_____
_____
_____
_____
_____
_____

Consider the instruction Mary gave the disciples at the wedding. She was bold and to the point, considering Jesus was about to perform His first miracle. How does this encourage your faith?

_____
_____
_____
_____
_____
_____

What benefits have you experienced in choosing to listen and act upon the Father's word?

_____
_____
_____
_____
_____

How do we hear His voice? What can you do to be more sensitive and receptive to His voice?

_____
_____
_____
_____
_____

Av 5781

Yom Rishon (1st Day)	Yom Sheni (2nd Day)	Yom Sh'lishi (3rd Day)	Yom Revi'i (4th Day)
Sunday	**Monday**	**Tuesday**	**Wednesday**
2 JULY 11 ✡Bein HaMetzarim (Between The Straits, Day 14/21)	3 JULY 12 ✡Bein HaMetzarim (Between The Straits, Day 15/21)	4 JULY 13 ✡Bein HaMetzarim (Between The Straits, Day 16/21)	5 JULY 14 ✡Bein HaMetzarim (Between The Straits, Day 17/21)
9 JULY 18 ✡Bein HaMetzarim (Between The Straits, Day 21/21) (Tammuz 18- Av 9) ✡Tisha B'Av (9th of Av)	10 JULY 19	11 JULY 20	12 JULY 21
16 JULY 25	17 JULY 26	18 JULY 27	19 JULY 28
23 AUG 1 30 AUG 8 ◐Rosh Chodesh ELUL	24 AUG 2	25 AUG 3	26 AUG 4

July/August 2021

Yom Chamishi (5th Day)	Yom Shishi (6th Day)	Yom Shabbat (The Shabbat)	Moed
Thursday	**Friday**	**Saturday**	**Season**
	TAMMUZ 29 JULY 9 ✡Bein HaMetzarim (Between The Straits, Day 12/21) ○Rosh Chodesh AV 🕯🕯*Shabbat begins*	1 JULY 10 ✡Bein HaMetzarim (Between The Straits, Day 13/21) ○Rosh Chodesh AV 🕯*Shabbat ends*	**Kaitz (Summer)** *Season of Preparation*
6 JULY 15 ✡Bein HaMetzarim (Between The Straits, Day 18/21)	7 JULY 16 ✡Bein HaMetzarim (Between The Straits, Day 19/21) 🕯🕯 *Shabbat begins*	8 JULY 17 ✡Bein HaMetzarim (Between The Straits, Day 20/21) 🕯 *Shabbat ends*	**Months of Kaitz** Tammuz *Guarding Our Heart & Eyes* Av *Believing The Father's Goodness* Elul *The King is in The Field*
13 JULY 22	14 ●JULY 23 🕯🕯 *Shabbat begins*	15 JULY 24 ✡Tu B'Av (15th of Av) (Holiday of Love & Romance) 🕯 *Shabbat ends*	**Tribes of Kaitz** Reuven *Behold, A Son* Shimon *Gracious Hearing* Gad *A Troop, Good Fortune*
20 JULY 29	21 JULY 30 🕯🕯 *Shabbat begins*	22 JULY 31 🕯 *Shabbat ends*	**Notes**
27 AUG 5	28 AUG 6 🕯🕯 *Shabbat begins*	29 AUG 7 🕯 *Shabbat ends*	

Bible Portions for Av 5781

Read through the Torah in a year and glean from the Prophets and the New Testament.
Space provided for notes.

Week of:
Av 1, 5781/ July 10, 2021

Torah Portion: **Mattot** *(Tribes)* Num 30:1- 32:42
Prophets Portion: Jer 1:1- 2:3
NT Portion: Phil 3:12- 16

Torah Portions: **Massei** *(Journeys of)* Num 33:1- 36:13
Prophets Portions: Jer 2:4- 28, 3:4
NT Portion: James 4:1- 12

_____
_____
_____
_____
_____

Week of:
Av 8, 5781 / July 17, 2021

Torah Portion: **Devarim** *(Words)* Deut 1:1- 3:22
Prophets Portion: Isa 1:1- 27
NT Portion: 1 Tim 3:1- 7

_____
_____
_____

Week of:
Av 15, 5781 / July 24, 2021

Torah Portion: **Va'etchanan** *(And I pleaded)* Deut 3:23- 7:11
Prophets Portion: Isa 40:1- 26
NT Portion: Mark 12:28- 34

_____
_____

Week of:
Av 22, 5781 / July 31, 2021

Torah Portion: **Ekev** *(On the heel of, because)* Deut 7:12- 11:25
Prophets Portion: Isa 49:14- 51:3
NT Portion: Rom 8:31- 39

_____
_____
_____

Week of:
Av 29, 5781 / Aug 7, 2021

Torah Portion: **Re'eh** *(See)* Deut 11:26- 16:17
Prophets Portion: Isa 54:11- 55:5
NT Portion: John 4:1- 6

_____
_____
_____

Elul 5781

August 9 – September 6, 2021

Sixth Month of Spiritual Year
29 days

The King Is In The Field In Elul

We made it through Av… known as the "narrowest" month of the year. We have not shrunk back in unbelief. We decided to believe the good report of the Lord and have moved forward. We now find ourselves in a great expanse in this sixth month of the Biblical year called Elul. We have reached both the mid-point of the spiritual year and the last month of the civil year. It's a wide-open field. But wait… do you see what I see? There is someone in this field. Behold! The King is the in the field!

What does this mean? A king….in a field? That doesn't seem to go together. What is a person of royalty doing in an ordinary field? Shouldn't he be in his palace…sitting on his throne… surrounded by guards and ruling over important issues of his kingdom? Yes, this is the usual "modus operandi" of a king. However, historically, in Jewish tradition, there is one month of the year when the king leaves his palace and goes into the working fields of his kingdom to meet with his people. Normally, one would be summoned to his palace and go through check points to approach his throne room. But in Elul, the king comes to his people. He sets his royal tent in the fields of his people and they have access to meet him face to face.

Is this starting to sound familiar? This is another type and shadow of what Jesus did. The King of all Kings left His heavenly throne and dwelt among us. *"And the Word became flesh, and dwelt among us, and we saw His glory, glory as of the only begotten from the Father, full of grace and truth." (Jn 1:14)* He came down to earth because of His great love for the world. As the Bible tells us, *"In this is love, not that we loved God, but that He loved us and sent His Son to be the propitiation for our sins." (1 Jn 4:10)* In His great love for us, Jesus gave His life willingly so we could be reconciled back to the Father and have access to Him again. He wants to be King of the field of our hearts! When we receive Him in our hearts, He establishes His tent pegs permanently and we become His dwelling place forever. In Him, we have a much better covenant than just access one month a year. We have access 24/7, 365 days a year. He places His Spirit in us and seals us forever! (Jn 14:16-17, Eph 1:13-14). He invites us to a special time of intimacy in Elul. All we need to do is receive Him and His great love for us. In fact, the acronym for "Elul" itself is… *"I am my Beloved's and my Beloved is mine." (SOS 6:1)*

Elul is often referred to as "a haven in time." Psalm 27 is often read in Elul for this very reason. *"For in the day of trouble He will conceal me in His tabernacle. In the secret place of His tent He will hide me. He will lift me up on a rock. And now my head will be lifted up above my enemies around me and I will offer in His tent sacrifices with shouts of joy. I will sing, yes, I will sing praises to the Lord." (Ps 27:5-6)* As we open our hearts in His tent, the Master Gardener gives us wisdom on navigating those fields that concern us the most… the fields of our family, our marriage, our work and our ministry. He will personally instruct and walk with us in our fields of influence, our field of dreams and yes, even our battlefields. He knows exactly how to make our personal and unique fields fruitful. He is delighted to walk the fields with us, His beloved, just as we read in Song of Solomon 7:11… *"Come, my beloved, let us go out into the fields."*

As we walk with our King, He reveals His grace and truth over each allotted parcel He has given us. Perhaps we've allowed weeds to grow or overworked a field without letting it rest. Maybe we've been working a field for our own gain or perhaps have been sitting on the throne of our own "kingdom." As He reveals His lovingkindness over these areas, our eyes turn from self onto His Spirit within us. As we turn from our kingdom to His, our fields fall into proper order and begin to flourish, like His word says… *"Seek first His kingdom and His righteousness and all these things will be added to you." (Matt 6:33)* The Hebrew letter "Yod" underscores this point. It's the smallest letter in the alphabet, yet it carries great significance. Its curved shape depicts a humble position of repentance and mercy from the hand of God. His kindness leads to repentance. Repentance leads to mercy and fruitfulness. This is truly a gift from His hand. (Rom 2:4)

Lastly, as we hear the Lord's instruction over our portions, it's important we respond with obedience. Our left hand is highlighted this month, calling us to action, to fix what is broken. Let's put our hands to the plow, for He directs us to be doers of His word, and not merely hearers. (Lk 9:62, Js 1:22-25)

How are your fields growing? Do you need help tending them? Behold! The King is in your field! Run into His tent! Be refreshed and renewed knowing you are His beloved. He has many gifts to give you… wisdom, kindness, joy, mercy and love. Receive all His gifts, respond and take action! May you feel His smile upon you as you do! *"Draw me after You and let us run together! The King has brought me into His chambers." (SOS 1:4)*

Journal for Elul 5781

Use the space below to record your thoughts, praises and prayers for this month.

_____
_____
_____
_____
_____
_____
_____
_____
_____
_____
_____
_____
_____
_____
_____
_____
_____
_____
_____
_____
_____
_____
_____
_____
_____
_____
_____
_____
_____
_____
_____
_____
_____
_____
_____
_____
_____

Go to "Chalkboard Teachings" page at www.christinevales.com or scan QR Code below.
Enjoy watching the chalkboard teaching for this month. Use space below to take notes.

Scan QR code to go directly to "Chalkboard Teachings" page at www.christinevales.com.

98

Prophetic Fact Sheet for Elul 5781

BABYLONIAN NAME
ELUL
- "A Vain Thing", "Nothingness", "To Search
- Hebrew Acronym "Ani L'dodi V'dodi Li" =
"I am my beloved's and my beloved is mine" (SOS 6:3)

HEBREW NAME
6th MONTH
- Hebrew Letter Vav = 6
- A Tent Peg, Nail
- To Connect, Make Secure
- Man's Efforts

MONTH OF THE YEAR
6th MONTH OF SPIRITUAL YEAR
- Hebrew Letter Vav = 6
- A Tent Peg, Nail, To Connect, Make Secure, Man's Efforts

12th MONTH OF PHYSICAL/CIVIL YEAR
- Hebrew Letters Yod and Bet = 12
- Leadership, Government

SEASON (Moed)
KAITZ (Summer) • Season of Preparation

TRIBES of KAITZ • Reuven, Shimon, Gad

MONTHLY THEMES of KAITZ
- TAMMUZ • Guarding Our Heart & Eyes
- AV • Believing Abba
- ELUL • The King is in The Field

APPOINTED TIMES (Moedim)
ELUL 1
✿ROSH CHODESH ELUL (Head of Month, Elul)
- Ps 81:1-4
- Moses went up Mt Sinai after sin of golden calf
- Exo 34

**ELUL 1-
TISHERI 10
(Yom Kippur)**
✿YEMI RATZON (40 Days of Teshuvah/ Favor)
- "Teshuvah" = Repentance in Hebrew
- Also called "Days of Favor" as The Lord offered pardon and forgiveness to a repentant people after the sin of the golden calf

ELUL 20
✿SELICHOT ("Excuse Me")
- Meditate on attributes of God's Mercy (Ps 145)

COLOR/GEMSTONES
COLOR	Gray
GEMSTONE	Jasper, Hematite

TRIBE OF ISRAEL
GAD
- "A Troop or Camp", "Good Fortune"
- 7th Son of Ya'akov
- 1st Son by Le'ah's Maid, Zilpah (Gen 30:10-11)

- **Ya'akov Prophetic Blessing** (Gen 49:19) *"As for Gad, raiders shall raid him, but he will raid at their heels."*
  - Camped south of tabernacle w/Reuven & Shimon (Num 2)
  - Flag: Gray with a military camp on it (Gen 49:19)
  - Fierce warriors with the ability to organize a troop of men

HEBREW LETTER

YOD
- 10th Letter of the Hebrew Alphabet
- Numerical Value: 10 = Perfection, Divine Order
- Smallest letter in the Hebrew alphabet
- Closed Hand, The Hand of God
- Appointed mercy from The Hand of God
- Man Praying, Humility, Holiness, An Action, Work
- Godly Authority, Number of Order, Tithe, Testimony

ACTION/BODY PART
TO FIX
- To search, as in the heart in repentance
- To save a situation rather than throw it away

LEFT HAND
- Hand of action, Put your hand to the plow (Lk 9:62)
- Left side is your physical side (Isa 48:13)

CONSTELLATION
BETHULAH (Virgo)
- The Virgin
- "I am my beloved's and my beloved is mine" (SOS 6:3)
- God's beloved bride, Israel and the church

MONTHLY CHARACTERISTICS
- Month of repentance, mercy and forgiveness (Prov 28:13)
- Read Psalm 27 central to teshuvah (repentance)
- Time to fix what has been broken
- Time to get spiritual house in order
- Meditate on the "Parable of The Sower" (Mark 4)
- Month when "The King is in The Field" (SOS 6:2-3)
- Enter into intimacy with the Lord (Ps 45, SOS)
- All can approach Him (Zech 8:23, Matt 9:20-22, Heb 4:15-16)
- Seek first His kingdom- all added onto you (Matt 6:33)
- Meditate on God's unconditional love for you (1 Jn 4:10,18)
- Declare "I am the disciple Jesus loves" (Jn 13:23)
- Let His countenance shine on you (Exo 34:29, Num 6:22-27)
- Run into your Tower of Might (Prov 18:10)
- Find your place in "the company" of The Lord like Gad
- "Mother" month / Month of nurturing
- Month of spiritual service, organization, management
- Preparation for the "High Holy Days" in Tishrei
- Last month of the civil year

Elul 5781
Bible Study & Thought Questions
For Individual & Group Study

Dive into this portion of the New Testament for further reflection on the theme of the month. Ponder thought questions that follow and use space for personal reflection and group study.

Mark 4:1-20

He began to teach again by the sea. And such a very large crowd gathered to Him that He got into a boat in the sea and sat down; and the whole crowd was by the sea on the land. ² And He was teaching them many things in parables, and was saying to them in His teaching, ³ "Listen to this! Behold, the sower went out to sow; ⁴ as he was sowing, some seed fell beside the road, and the birds came and ate it up. ⁵ Other seed fell on the rocky ground where it did not have much soil; and immediately it sprang up because it had no depth of soil. ⁶ And after the sun had risen, it was scorched; and because it had no root, it withered away. ⁷ Other seed fell among the thorns, and the thorns came up and choked it, and it yielded no crop. ⁸ Other seeds fell into the good soil, and as they grew up and increased, they yielded a crop and produced thirty, sixty, and a hundredfold." ⁹ And He was saying, "He who has ears to hear, let him hear."

¹⁰ As soon as He was alone, His followers, along with the twelve, began asking Him about the parables. ¹¹ And He was saying to them, "To you has been given the mystery of the kingdom of God, but those who are outside get everything in parables, ¹² so that while seeing, they may see and not perceive, and while hearing, they may hear and not understand, otherwise they might return and be forgiven." ¹³ And He said to them, "Do you not understand this parable? How will you understand all the parables? ¹⁴ The sower sows the word. ¹⁵ These are the ones who are beside the road where the word is sown; and when they hear, immediately Satan comes and takes away the word which has been sown in them. ¹⁶ In a similar way these are the ones on whom seed was sown on the rocky places, who, when they hear the word, immediately receive it with joy; ¹⁷ and they have no firm root in themselves, but are only temporary; then, when affliction or persecution arises because of the word, immediately they fall away. ¹⁸ And others are the ones on whom seed was sown among the thorns; these are the ones who have heard the word, ¹⁹ but the worries of the world, and the deceitfulness of riches, and the desires for other things enter in and choke the word, and it becomes unfruitful. ²⁰ And those are the ones on whom seed was sown on the good soil; and they hear the word and accept it and bear fruit, thirty, sixty, and a hundredfold."

Thought Questions for Elul 5781

What are the four types of soil described in Mark 4 and what do they yield?

_____
_____
_____
_____
_____
_____

What does the soil represent? What does the seed represent?

_____
_____
_____
_____
_____
_____

In this month where we meditate on how the King is in our field, the most important field is that of our hearts. How would you describe the condition of the soil of your heart?

_____
_____
_____
_____
_____
_____

How can you better prepare the soil of your heart?

_____
_____
_____
_____
_____

As you walk the fields with Him - what seeds have been planted and what fruit has been produced?

_____
_____
_____
_____
_____
_____

Elul 5781

Yom Rishon (1st Day)	Yom Sheni (2nd Day)	Yom Sh'lishi (3rd Day)	Yom Revi'i (4th Day)
Sunday	**Monday**	**Tuesday**	**Wednesday**
AV 30 AUG 8 ○Rosh Chodesh ELUL	1 AUG 9 ✿Yemi Ratzon (40 Days of Teshuvah/Favor) (Elul 1 - Tishrei 10) ○Rosh Chodesh ELUL	2 AUG 10	3 AUG 11
7 AUG 15	8 AUG 16	9 AUG 17	10 AUG 18
14 ●AUG 22	15 AUG 23	16 AUG 24	17 AUG 25
21 AUG 29	22 AUG 30	23 AUG 31	24 SEPT 1
28 SEPT 5	29 SEPT 6 ○Rosh Hashanah 5782 (Head of The Year)		

August/September 2021

Yom Chamishi (5th Day)	Yom Shishi (6th Day)	Yom Shabbat (The Shabbat)	Moed
Thursday	**Friday**	**Saturday**	**Season**
4 AUG 12	5 AUG 13 🕯🕯 *Shabbat begins*	6 AUG 14 🕯 *Shabbat ends*	**Kaitz (Summer)** *Season of Preparation*
11 AUG 19	12 AUG 20 🕯🕯 *Shabbat begins*	13 AUG 21 🕯 *Shabbat ends*	**Months of Kaitz** Tammuz *Guarding Our Heart & Eyes* Av *Believing The Father's Goodness* Elul *The King is in The Field*
18 AUG 26	19 AUG 27 🕯🕯 *Shabbat begins*	20 AUG 28 ✡Selichot ("Excuse Me") 🕯 *Shabbat ends*	**Tribes of Kaitz** Reuven *Behold, A Son* Shimon *Gracious Hearing* Gad *A Troop, Good Fortune*
25 SEPT 2	26 SEPT 3 🕯🕯 *Shabbat begins*	27 SEPT 4 🕯 *Shabbat ends*	**Notes**

Bible Portions for Elul 5781

Read through the Torah in a year and glean from the Prophets and the New Testament.
Space provided for notes.

Week of:
Elul 6, 5781/ Aug 14, 2021

Torah Portion: **Shoftim** *(Judges)* Deut 16:18- 21:9
Prophets Portion: Isa 51:12- 52:12
NT Portion: John 1:19- 27

_____

_____

_____

_____

_____

Week of:
Elul 13, 5781/ Aug 21, 2021

Torah Portion: **Ki Tetze** *(When you go out)* Deut 21:10- 25:19
Prophets Portion: Isa 54:1- 10
NT Portion: 1 Cor 5:1- 5

_____

_____

_____

_____

_____

Week of:
Elul 20, 5781/ Aug 28, 2021

Torah Portion: **Ki Tavo** *(When you go in)* Deut 26:1- 29:8
Prophets Portion: Isa 60:1- 22
NT Portion: Acts 7:30- 36

_____

_____

_____

_____

_____

Week of:
Elul 27, 5781/ Sept 4, 2021

Torah Portion: **Nitzavim** *(Standing)* Deut 29:9- 30:20
Prophets Portion: Isa 61:10- 63:9
NT Portion: Rom 10:1- 13

_____

_____

_____

_____

_____

Tishrei 5782

September 7 – October 6, 2021

Seventh Month of Spiritual Year
30 days

Blast-Off Into Tishrei

Three, Two, One…Blast-off! Welcome to Tishrei! The seventh month of the Biblical year starts off with a blast! It's the blast of the shofar! This blast welcomes the first day of the month, known as the "Feast of Trumpets." It is a call to "Awake!" Literally a "wake-up call" from the Lord for believers and non-believers alike. This season is all about awakening our hearts to return to the Lord. This is something we would not normally do on our own. The Lord knows we have a tendency to drift, so in His great love for us, He initiated a season to keep us in communion with Him. We hear His shofar blast several times in this month of "The High Holidays." Now that He has our attention… let us tune in to hear His word.

We hear a second blow of the shofar at the top of this month calling us to "Return!" In the Old Testament, this marks the ten-day countdown known as "The Days of Awe." This is a time of reflection and returning. The Hebrew letter of the month, "Lamed" pictures a shepherd's staff which gently directs sheep back to their Shepherd, their absolute source. At the end of these ten days, the shofar blasts again calling us to "Repent!" This is called "The Day of Atonement" also known as "Yom Kippur." This is the holiest day on the Hebrew calendar marked by fasting and confession. The Hebrew word "kippur" means "covering" and on Yom Kippur the High Priest would confess the sins of Israel by laying his hands on the head of a goat. The goat would then "take on" the sin of the nation and be sacrificed on Israel's behalf. The Lord would then accept the blood offering and extend forgiveness to Israel, thus Israel would be "covered" for another year.

But what about us today? God required the blood of an animal for the atonement of sin in the Old Testament (Lev 17:11) But this atonement only covered sin. It did not erase it completely. Therefore, He made a new and better covenant with us in the New Testament through the blood of His own Son. *"He made Him (Jesus) who had no sin to be sin for us, so that in Him we might become the righteousness of God." (2 Cor 5:21)* Jesus was the perfect sacrifice and "took on" sin just as the goat did, only better… much better! Jesus took on the sin of the whole world and His blood erased it once and for all! The ultimate sacrifice was offered and accepted by the Lord. Now the question remains… have we accepted Jesus' blood on our behalf? When we do, the divine exchange takes place. He took our sin so we could take on His righteousness. Whether we are responding to His call for the first time or rededicating our hearts, may we come before Him with a humble heart like David saying, *"Search me, O God, and know my heart. Try me and know my anxious thoughts and see if there be any hurtful way in me and lead me in the everlasting way." (Ps 139:23-24)* His kindness leads us to repentance and ultimately brings joy and peace with God. Hence the shofar blasts… calling us to Awake! Return! Repent! (Rom 2:4)

A final blast rings as the full moon hangs in the night sky. This blast calls us to "Rejoice!" and begins the "Feast of Tabernacles" or "Succot." This week-long feast not only celebrates the Lord's physical provision of the fall harvest, but also rejoices in the spiritual provision of the Lord Himself, who literally tabernacles in our very midst. As believers, we are the tabernacles of God, as His Spirit resides in us forever. One of the joys of this feast is celebrating in our own tabernacle or tent. (Lev 23:42) The Lord appointed this time for us to rejoice in our tents, reminding us of His great faithfulness to the Israelites tenting in the wilderness and to us! As we gather in our tent or "sukkah" with family and friends, it's the grand finale of this season and time for all to rejoice in the faithfulness of our Good Shepherd for *"In His presence is fullness of joy!." (Ps 16:11)*

Lastly, Tishrei means "beginning." After hearing and discovering the meaning of each shofar blast, we can clearly hear His invitation. Old habits and cycles end and new life begins. This coincides with the new civil year, which begins on Tishrei 1, Rosh Hashanah. This year, the numerical year turns from 5781 to 5782. The Hebrew letter "Pey" has a value of eighty and depicts a divine beginning or opening. It also symbolizes a mouth speaking forth a command. The number two is connected with the letter "Bet" and depicts a home, tent, the body or household. It also means to be inside or within. Let us continue abiding in Him in and through 5782 and declare His truth over our homes and bodies, for He is literally in our midst.

Do you hear the Lord's wake-up call? What is He calling you to turn from? Have you personally accepted Jesus' blood sacrifice as payment for your sin? May you and your family consider celebrating His faithfulness by rejoicing in your own tent on Succot. Take heed of each blast of the shofar this month and respond with a humble heart. The Lord knows us well. In His great love, He gives us a wake-up call so we can blast-off into the new as a new creation in Him! *"Therefore if anyone is in Christ, they are a new creation. Old things are passed away, behold, all things are made new." (2 Cor 5:17)*

Journal for Tishrei 5782

Use the space below to record your thoughts, praises and prayers for this month.

_____
_____
_____
_____
_____
_____
_____
_____
_____
_____
_____
_____
_____
_____
_____
_____
_____
_____
_____
_____
_____
_____
_____
_____
_____
_____
_____
_____
_____
_____
_____
_____
_____

Chalkboard Teaching for Tishrei 5782

Go to "Chalkboard Teachings" page at www.christinevales.com or scan QR Code below.
Enjoy watching the chalkboard teaching for this month. Use space below to take notes.

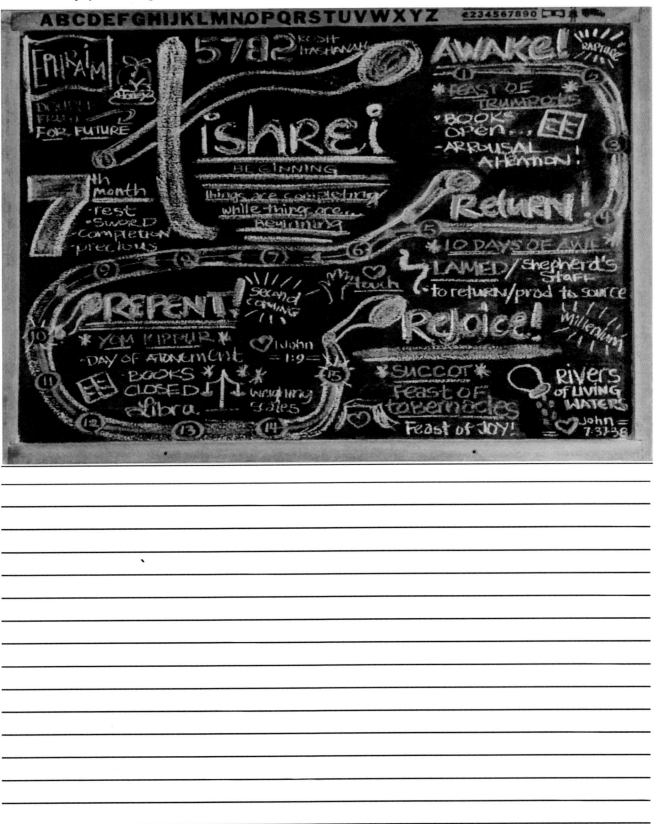

Scan QR code to go directly to "Chalkboard Teachings" page at www.christinevales.com.

108

Prophetic Fact Sheet for Tishrei 5782

BABYLONIAN NAME

TISHREI
- "The Beginning"
- From Hebrew "Reishit"= Beginning
- First word in the first book (Gen 1:1)

HEBREW NAME

ETHANIM
- "Steady, Ever-Flowing Streams"

MONTH OF THE YEAR

7th MONTH OF SPIRITUAL YEAR
- Hebrew Letter Zayin = 7
- Completion, Perfection, Rest, A Sword
- 7's are important and dear to The Lord

1st MONTH OF PHYSICAL/CIVIL YEAR
- Hebrew Letter Aleph = 1
- Beginning, Abba, Ox, Head, Unity, To Teach

SEASON (Moed)

STAV (Fall)
- Season of Repentance

TRIBES of STAV
- Efrayim, Menashe, Binyamiyn

MONTHLY THEMES of STAV

TISHREI
- Month of Returning & Rejoicing

CHESHVAN
- New Beginnings

KISLEV
- Month of Hope

APPOINTED TIMES (Moedim)

TISHREI 1
✿ROSH HASHANAH (Head of The Year)
- Num 29:1, Lev 23:24

TISHREI 1
✿YOM TERU'AH (Feast of Trumpets, Awake!)
- Day of Judgment, Day "The Books" are open
- Lev 25:9, Num 10:5-6

TISHREI 1-
TISHREI 10
✿YAMIM NORAIM (Days of Awe)
- Tishrei 1-10 (Last ten days of Yemi Ratzon)

ELUL 1-
TISHREI 10
✿YEMI RATZON (40 Days of Teshuvah/ Favor)
- "Teshuvah" - Repentance in Hebrew
- The Lord extended grace after sin of golden calf

TISHREI 10
✿YOM KIPPUR (Day of Atonement, Repent!)
- Moses descended Mt Sinai 40 days from Elul 1 with the new tablets of 10 Commandments
- Ex 34:29
- Day "The Books" are closed
- Lev 17:11, 23:27

TISHREI 15-21
✿SUCCOT (Feast of Tabernacles, Rejoice!)
- Lev 23:24, Deut 16:13

TISHREI 22
✿SHIMI ATZERET (8th Day of Assembly)
- Num 29:35

TISHREI 23
✿SIMCHAT TORAH (Rejoicing with The Torah)
- Lev 23:24, Num 29:35

✿**NOTE:** Many Biblical scholars believe that Messiah was born in Tishrei, during Succot. Emmanuel, God tabernacles with us. Something to ponder...

COLOR/GEMSTONES

COLOR	Black
GEMSTONES	Black Onyx, Agate

TRIBE OF ISRAEL

EFRAYIM (Ephraim)
- "Double Fruitfulness"
- 2nd Son of Yosef (Joesph)
- 2nd Son by Asenath (Gen 41:52)

Ya'akov's Prophetic Blessing (Gen 48:14-16, 20) *"But Yisra'el stretched out his right hand and laid it on the head of Efrayim who was the younger, and his left hand on Menashe's head, crossing his hands, although Menashe was the firstborn. He blessed Yosef, and said, "The God before whom my fathers Avraham and Ya'akov walked, The God who has been my shepherd all my life to this day, The angel who has redeemed me from all evil, Bless the lads, and may my name live on in them, and the names of my fathers, Avraham and Ya'akov, and may they grow into a multitude in the midst of the earth." Ya'akov blessed them that day saying, "By you, Yisra'el will pronounce blessing, saying, 'May God make you like Efrayim and Menashe!' Thus he put Efrayim before Menashe."*

YOSEF (Joseph)
- "Adonai Brings Increase"
- 11th Son of Ya'akov (Jacob)
- 1st Son by Rachel (Gen 30:22-24)

Ya'akov's Prophetic Blessing (Gen 49:22-26) *"Yosef is a fruitful bough, a fruitful bough by a spring. Its branches run over a wall. The archers bitterly attacked him and shot at him and harassed him, but his bow remained firm and his arms were agile, from the hands of the Mighty One of Ya'akov (From there is the Shepherd, the Stone of Yisra'el). From the God of your father who helps you and by the Almighty who blesses you with blessings of heaven above, blessings of the deep that lies beneath, blessings of the breasts and of the womb. The blessings of your father have surpassed the blessings of my ancestors, up to the utmost bound of the everlasting hills. May they be on the head of Yosef and on the crown of the head of the one distinguished among his brothers."*

- Camped west of tabernacle w/Menashe & Binyamiyn (Num 2)
- Flag: Black with bull (Efrayim) & ox (Menashe) (Deut 33:17)
- Efrayim was blessed as the

HEBREW LETTER

LAMED
- 12th Letter of the Hebrew Alphabet
- Numerical Value: 30
- Perfection of Divine Order
- Tallest and central letter of the Hebrew alphabet
- Return to your absolute Source, The Lord Adonai His authority
- A Shepherd's Staff, To Teach, Point, Goad, Prod Toward

ACTION/BODY PART

TOUCH	Touch the hem of His garment (Matt 9:20-22)
GALLBLADDER	

CONSTELLATION

MOZANAIM (Libra)
- The Scales Weighing
- Deeds of man weighed for judgment
- "The Books" open on Rosh Hashanah & close on Yom Kippur
- But now: Under a New and Better Covenant (Heb 7-9)

MONTHLY CHARACTERISTICS

- Returning to your absolute source/ The Lord Adonai
- Month of return, repentance and rejoicing
- Experience His mercy and forgiveness
- Time to awake from slumber (Eph 5:14-21)
- Repentance: a gift from God/ Brings peace w/ Him (Rom 2:4)
- Time to remove hindrances / Keep flow clear
- Follow the lead of the Good Shepherd (Jn 10:1-30)
- "Head of the Year"/ Civil calendar year advances
- Notice the justice system / Month of Justice (Rom 12:19)
- A well-balanced control of activity
- Things finishing and beginning simultaneously
- Celebrate the New and Better Covenant (Heb 7-9)

Tishrei 5782
Bible Study & Thought Questions
For Individual & Group Study

Dive into this portion of the New Testament for further reflection on the theme of the month. Ponder thought questions that follow and use space for personal reflection and group study.

Luke 15:11-32

11 And He said, "A man had two sons. **12** The younger of them said to his father, 'Father, give me the share of the estate that falls to me.' So he divided his wealth between them. **13** And not many days later, the younger son gathered everything together and went on a journey into a distant country, and there he squandered his estate with loose living. **14** Now when he had spent everything, a severe famine occurred in that country, and he began to be impoverished. **15** So he went and hired himself out to one of the citizens of that country, and he sent him into his fields to feed swine. **16** And he would have gladly filled his stomach with the pods that the swine were eating, and no one was giving anything to him. **17** But when he came to his senses, he said, 'How many of my father's hired men have more than enough bread, but I am dying here with hunger! **18** I will get up and go to my father, and will say to him, "Father, I have sinned against heaven, and in your sight; **19** I am no longer worthy to be called your son; make me as one of your hired men."' **20** So he got up and came to his father. But while he was still a long way off, his father saw him and felt compassion for him, and ran and embraced him and kissed him. **21** And the son said to him, 'Father, I have sinned against heaven and in your sight; I am no longer worthy to be called your son.' **22** But the father said to his slaves, 'Quickly bring out the best robe and put it on him, and put a ring on his hand and sandals on his feet; **23** and bring the fattened calf, kill it, and let us eat and celebrate; **24** for this son of mine was dead and has come to life again; he was lost and has been found.' And they began to celebrate.

25 "Now his older son was in the field, and when he came and approached the house, he heard music and dancing. **26** And he summoned one of the servants and began inquiring what these things could be. **27** And he said to him, 'Your brother has come, and your father has killed the fattened calf because he has received him back safe and sound.' **28** But he became angry and was not willing to go in; and his father came out and began pleading with him. **29** But he answered and said to his father, 'Look! For so many years I have been serving you and I have never neglected a command of yours; and yet you have never given me a young goat, so that I might celebrate with my friends; **30** but when this son of yours came, who has devoured your wealth with prostitutes, you killed the fattened calf for him.' **31** And he said to him, 'Son, you have always been with me, and all that is mine is yours. **32** But we had to celebrate and rejoice, for this brother of yours was dead and has begun to live, and was lost and has been found.'"

Thought Questions for Tishrei 5782

The passage in Luke says the father saw his son from a distance. What does that tell you about the heart of God for us when we repent?

_____
_____
_____
_____
_____
_____

What is the root cause of the sin in both sons?

_____
_____
_____
_____
_____
_____

God offers forgiveness and reconciliation and wants to give us joy as well. How does this encourage you?

_____
_____
_____
_____
_____
_____

The Lord is highlighting repentance this month. Repentance is a gift that brings peace with Him. After meditating on the truths in this passage, has your view of repentance changed? If so, how?

_____
_____
_____
_____
_____

Have you experienced God's unconditional forgiveness? Expand on that. If not, what barriers stand in your way of the Father's love for you and what actions can you take?

_____
_____
_____
_____
_____

Tishrei 5782

Yom Rishon (1st Day)	Yom Sheni (2nd Day)	Yom Sh'lishi (3rd Day)	Yom Revi'i (4th Day)
Sunday	**Monday**	**Tuesday**	**Wednesday**
	ELUL 29 SEPT 6 ○Rosh Hashanah 5782 (Head of The Year)	**1** SEPT 7 ✡Yom Teru'ah (Feast of Trumpets) ✡Yamim Noraim (Days of Awe, Day 1/10) ○Rosh Hashanah 5782 (Head of The Year)	**2** SEPT 8 ✡Yamim Noraim (Days of Awe, Day 2/10)
6 SEPT 12 ✡Yamim Noraim (Days of Awe, Day 6/10)	**7** SEPT 13 ✡Yamim Noraim (Days of Awe, Day 7/10)	**8** SEPT 14 ✡Yamim Noraim (Days of Awe, Day 8/10)	**9** SEPT 15 ✡Yamim Noraim (Days of Awe, Day 9/10)
13 SEPT 19	**14** ●SEPT 20	**15** SEPT 21 ✡Succot (Feast of Tabernacles, Day 1)	**16** SEPT 22 ✡Succot (Feast of Tabernacles, Day 2)
20 SEPT 26 ✡Succot (Feast of Tabernacles, Day 6)	**21** SEPT 27 ✡Succot (Feast of Tabernacles, Day 7)	**22** SEPT 28 ✡Shimi Atzeret (8th Day of Assembly)	**23** SEPT 29 ✡Simchat Torah (Rejoicing with The Torah)
27 OCT 3	**28** OCT 4	**29** OCT 5	**30** OCT 6 ○Rosh Chodesh CHESHVAN

September/October 2021

Yom Chamishi (5th Day)	Yom Shishi (6th Day)	Yom Shabbat (The Shabbat)	Moed
Thursday	**Friday**	**Saturday**	**Season**
3 SEPT 9 ✡Yamim Noraim (Days of Awe, Day 3/10)	**4** SEPT 10 ✡Yamim Noraim (Days of Awe, Day 4/10) 👐 *Shabbat begins*	**5** SEPT 11 ✡Yamim Noraim (Days of Awe, Day 5/10) 🕯 *Shabbat ends*	**Stav (Fall)** *Season of Repentance*
10 SEPT 16 ✡Yemi Ratzon Ends (Elul 1-Tishrei 10) ✡Yamim Noraim (Days of Awe, Day 10/10) ✡ Yom Kippur (Day of Atonement)	**11** SEPT 17 👐 *Shabbat begins*	**12** SEPT 18 🕯 *Shabbat ends*	**Months of Stav** Tishrei *Month of Returning & Rejoicing* Cheshvan *New Beginnings* Kislev *Month of Hope*
17 SEPT 23 ✡Succot (Feast of Tabernacles, Day 3)	**18** SEPT 24 ✡Succot (Feast of Tabernacles, Day 4) 👐 *Shabbat begins*	**19** SEPT 25 ✡Succot (Feast of Tabernacles, Day 5) 🕯 *Shabbat ends*	**Tribes of Stav** Efrayim *Be Fruitful and Mulitiply* Menashe *He Made Me to Forget* Binyamiyn *Son of My Right Hand*
24 SEPT 30	**25** OCT 1 👐 *Shabbat begins*	**26** OCT 2 🕯 *Shabbat ends*	**Notes**

Bible Portions for Tishrei 5782

Read through the Torah in a year and glean from the Prophets and the New Testament.
Space provided for notes.

Week of:
Tishrei 5, 5782/ Sept 11, 2021

Torah Portion: **Vayelech** *(And he went)* Deut 31:1- 30
Prophets Portion: Isa 55:6- 56:8
NT Portion: Rom 7:7- 12

_____

_____

_____

_____

_____

_____

Week of:
Tishrei 12, 5782/ Sept 18, 2021

Torah Portion: **Ha'azinu** *(Give ear)* Deut 32:1- 52
Prophets Portion: 2 Sam 22:1- 51
NT Portion: Rom 10:14- 11:12

_____

_____

_____

_____

_____

_____

Week of: *Holiday Readings*
Tishrei 19, 5782/ Sept 25, 2021

Torah Portion: Exo 33:12- 34:26
Prophets Portion: Eze 38:18- 39:16
NT Portion: 1 Thes 5:1- 11

_____

_____

_____

_____

_____

_____

Week of:
Tishrei 26, 5782/ Oct 2, 2021

Torah Portion: **B'reisheet** *(In the beginning)* Gen 1:1- 6:8
Prophets Portion: Isa 42:5- 43:10
NT Portion: John 1:1- 5

_____

_____

_____

_____

_____

_____

Cheshvan 5782

October 7 – November 4, 2021

Eighth Month of Spiritual Year
29 days

Cheshvan... A New Beginning Floods In

Katrina and Sandy... Irma and Dorian. These are familiar names of devastating hurricanes that hit the United States in the last decade. 'Tis the "hurricane season" and as you might suspect, this season of flooding is nothing new to the Lord. In fact, it was established long ago on God's calendar. Yes, Cheshvan is the month of Noah's great flood. It's also the eighth month connected with "new beginnings." So let's uncover Cheshvan and see how we can emerge from its waters stronger than ever!

If you have been tracking along with His calendar, you'll recall we just completed Tishrei, which means "beginning." Two back-to-back months about beginnings? Is this a typo? No, not at all! In order for us to go back to the "beginning", we have to have a "new" beginning. If we want to go back to Eden, where there was peace with God, we have to have a new beginning. Jesus even says this in the gospels... we must be born-again. This new birth happens when confess with our mouths and believe in our hearts that Jesus is Lord. (Rom 10:9) If you have never experienced this new birth, today is the day of salvation and is the perfect time to become a new creation in Him in this month of new beginnings! (Jn 3:3-8, 2 Cor 5:17-21, 1 Jn 1:1-10)

Most of us would not associate a fresh start with a flood, but the Lord did. Why did the He bring the flood upon the earth? We find the answer in His word... *"And God looked upon the world and saw how debased it was, for all humanity had corrupted their way upon the earth and lost their true direction." (Gen 6:12)* The Lord saw how corrupt the world was, with no chance to plant a seed of redemption for fallen man, because the enemy once again seduced and confused man. But Noah found favor in the sight of the Lord. *"But I will establish My covenant with you, Noah, and you shall enter the ark, you and your sons and your wife, and your sons' wives with you." (Gen 6:18)* In His mercy, He brought the flood upon the world so He could preserve the seed of the Redeemer.

Genesis 7 reveals the flood began on Cheshvan 17. Although it did rain for forty days and forty nights, we learn the waters covered the earth for one hundred and fifty days. *"Behold, I, even I am bringing the flood of water upon the earth, to destroy all flesh in which is the breath of life, from under heaven, everything that is on the earth shall perish." (Gen 8:17)* Genesis also reveals it was a year and ten days later, on Cheshvan 27, when the waters receded and Noah exited the ark. The ark is a picture of Jesus and a lesson for us today. When floodwaters rise in our lives, run into the Ark of Jesus and find safety and rest in His presence.

What happens when floodwaters move in? They move things around and expose things... like roots! The Lord uses the water of His Holy Spirit to reveal our actual root systems. He lovingly uncovers roots of bitterness or unforgiveness in our hearts and may unearth relational root systems with family, friends and others in order to bring wholeness to our lives. He desires to "get to the bottom" of health and financial concerns so we can start anew. He just doesn't leave us with our roots hanging out. When He reveals, He heals and gives us rest. As His word says... *"For the earth will be filled of the knowledge of the Lord, as the waters cover the sea. In that day, The Root of Jesse, Jesus, will stand as a banner for all peoples. The nations will rally to Him and His resting place will be glorious." (Isa 11:9-10)* Let us connect to The Root of Jesse and find our resting place in Him even now.

Lastly, we will notice there are no "appointed times" in Cheshvan. No feasts or fasts. Nothing. Silence. For this reason, the Jews say Cheshvan is "reserved" for Messiah's coming, as it is the only month with a vacancy to host such an occasion. Even the Hebrew letter of the month, "Nun", depicts an heir, an offspring, a son... a Messiah! Scripture does tell us... *"For the coming of the Son of Man will be just like the days of Noah." (Matt 24:37)* Does this mean Messiah's second coming could be in Cheshvan? The previous verse declares... *"But of that day and hour no one knows, not even the angels of heaven, nor the Son, but the Father alone." (Matt 24:36)* No one knows but the Father Himself, yet as believers, we can know *the season* and are commanded to be sober and awake, ready for His return at anytime. (1 Thes 5:1-9)

In this month of new beginnings, have you experienced the new birth in Christ? Receive Him and a fresh revelation of His love. His perfect love will cast out fear and will ready you for the return of your Beloved. If you feel the waters rising this month, run into the Ark of Jesus. He is your salvation during the storms of life. Remember He calms the seas and brings us to a safe haven. He is a gentle Master. What root issues are unearthing in your life? Allow Him to be The Root of your life and may your heart testify... *"His compassion never ends. It is only the Lord's mercies that have kept us from complete destruction. Great is his faithfulness. His loving-kindness begins afresh each day." (Lam 3:22-23)*

116

Journal for Cheshvan 5782

Use the space below to record your thoughts, praises and prayers for this month.

_____
_____
_____
_____
_____
_____
_____
_____
_____
_____
_____
_____
_____
_____
_____
_____
_____
_____
_____
_____
_____
_____
_____
_____
_____
_____
_____
_____
_____
_____
_____
_____
_____
_____
_____
_____
_____

Chalkboard Teaching for Cheshvan 5782

Go to "Chalkboard Teachings" page at www.christinevales.com or scan QR Code below.
Enjoy watching the chalkboard teaching for this month. Use space below to take notes.

Scan QR code to go directly to "Chalkboard Teachings" page at www.christinevales.com.

118

Prophetic Fact Sheet for Cheshvan 5782

BABYLONIAN NAME
CHESHVAN • "Eighth", "New Beginnings "

HEBREW NAME
BUL • "Produce" (In The Sense of Rain)

MONTH OF THE YEAR
8th MONTH OF SPIRITUAL YEAR
- Hebrew Letter Chet = 8
- A Fence, Chamber, Heart, To Protect or Separate
- New Beginnings, Letter of Life

2nd MONTH OF PHYSICAL/CIVIL YEAR
- Hebrew Letter Bet = 2
- A House, Tent, Household, Body

SEASON (Moed)
STAV (Fall) • Season of Repentance

TRIBES of STAV • Efrayim, Menashe, Binyamiyn

MONTHLY THEMES of STAV
TISHERI	• Month of Returning & Rejoicing
CHESHVAN	• New Beginnings
KISLEV	• Month of Hope

APPOINTED TIMES (Moedim)
CHESHVAN 1 ✿ROSH CHODESH CHESHVAN
(Head of Month, Cheshvan)
- Ps 81:1-4

✿**Something to Note…**
- This is the only month with no appointed times
- Jews believe this month is reserved for Messiah who will inaugurate the third temple

✿**Dates to Note…**
- Cheshvan 10   Noah ("Rest") entered the ark (Gen 7:1-5)
- Cheshvan 17   The flood began (Gen 7:10-11)
- Cheshvan 27   Noah exited the ark, a year later (Gen 8:14-20)

COLOR/GEMSTONES
| COLOR | Black |
| GEMSTONES | Black Onyx, Agate |

TRIBE OF ISRAEL
MENASHE (Manasseh) • "He Made Me to Forget"
- Firstborn Son of Yosef (Joeseph)
- 1st Son by Asenath (Gen 41:51)

Ya'akov's Prophetic Blessing (Gen 48:14-16, 20) *"But Yisra'el stretched out his right hand and laid it on the head of Efrayim who was the younger, and his left hand on Menashe's head, crossing his hands, although Menashe was the firstborn. He blessed Yosef, and said, "The God before whom my fathers Avraham and Ya'akov walked, The God who has been my shepherd all my life to this day, The angel who has redeemed me from all evil, Bless the lads, and may my name live on in them, and the names of my fathers, Avraham and Ya'akov, and may they grow into a multitude in the midst of the earth." Ya'akov blessed them that day saying, "By you, Yisra'el will pronounce blessing, saying, 'May God make you like Efrayim and Menashe!' Thus he put Efrayim before Menashe."*

YOSEF (Joseph) • "Adonai Brings Increase"
- 11th Son of Ya'akov (Jacob)
- 1st Son by Rachel (Gen 30:22-24)

Ya'akov's Prophetic Blessing (Gen 49:22-26) *"Yosef is a fruitful bough, a fruitful bough by a spring. Its branches run over a wall. The archers bitterly attacked him and shot at him and harassed him, but his bow remained firm and his arms were agile, from the hands of the Mighty One of Ya'akov (From there is the Shepherd, the Stone of Yisra'el). From the God of your father who helps you and by the Almighty who blesses you with blessings of heaven above, blessings of the deep that lies beneath, blessings of the breasts and of the womb. The blessings of your father have surpassed the blessings of my ancestors, up to the utmost bound of the everlasting hills. May they be on the head of Yosef and on the crown of the head of the one distinguished among his brothers."*
- Camped west of tabernacle w/Efrayim & Binyamiyn (Num 2)
- Flag: Black with bull (Efrayim) & ox (Menashe) (Deut 33:17)
- Efrayim blessed as the firstborn (Gen 48:20, Deut 33:17-19)

HEBREW LETTER

NUN
- 14th Letter of the Hebrew Alphabet
- Numerical Value 50
- Jubilee, Restoration, Pentecost, Release
- Messiah, Offspring, Heir, Son, Seed
- To Sprout, Spread, Continue
- A Fish Moving, Activity, Life

ACTION/BODY PART
SMELL • We are a fragrance of Christ to God (2 Cor 2:15-16)
INTESTINE • Digest what you have heard

CONSTELLATION
AKRAB (Scorpio)
- Scorpion, Wounding or Conflict
- Tread on serpents & scorpions (Gen 3:15, Lk 10:19, Jn 3:14-15)

MONTHLY CHARACTERISTICS
- Month of Messiah "Anointed One"
- Meditate on true ID/Anointed/Royal Priesthood (1 Pet 2:9)
- Month of the flood of Noah (see "Dates to Note")
- Run into ark of Jesus /Salvation & Rest (Ps 62:1, Matt 11:28)
- Month of the early rains (Joel 2:13)
- Floods reveal roots/ He reveals to heal (Ex 15:26, Jn 6:63)
- Connect with Jesus, "Root of Jesse" (Isa 11:9-10)
- Meditate upon "the days of Noah" (Matt 24:36-17, 1 Thes 5:1-9)
- Receive fresh revelation from His word
- Month to step on scorpions and serpents (Lk 10:19-20)
- Activate your ability to dissect and assimilate things
- War w/words/ Words you speak & receive (Prov 18:21)
- Words connect with your digestion
- "Eat The Word" (Jer 15:16, Eze 3:3)

Cheshvan 5782
Bible Study & Thought Questions
For Individual & Group Study

Dive into this portion of the New Testament for further reflection on the theme of the month. Ponder thought questions that follow and use space for personal reflection and group study.

John 3:1-21

Now there was a man of the Pharisees, named Nicodemus, a ruler of the Jews;[2] this man came to Jesus by night and said to Him, "Rabbi, we know that You have come from God as a teacher; for no one can do these signs that You do unless God is with him." [3] Jesus answered and said to him, "Truly, truly, I say to you, unless one is born-again he cannot see the kingdom of God."

[4] Nicodemus said to Him, "How can a man be born when he is old? He cannot enter a second time into his mother's womb and be born, can he?" [5] Jesus answered, "Truly, truly, I say to you, unless one is born of water and the Spirit he cannot enter into the kingdom of God. [6] That which is born of the flesh is flesh, and that which is born of the Spirit is spirit. [7] Do not be amazed that I said to you, 'You must be born-again.' [8] The wind blows where it wishes and you hear the sound of it, but do not know where it comes from and where it is going; so is everyone who is born of the Spirit."

[9] Nicodemus said to Him, "How can these things be?" [10] Jesus answered and said to him, "Are you the teacher of Israel and do not understand these things? [11] Truly, truly, I say to you, we speak of what we know and testify of what we have seen, and you do not accept our testimony. [12] If I told you earthly things and you do not believe, how will you believe if I tell you heavenly things? [13] No one has ascended into heaven, but He who descended from heaven: the Son of Man. [14] As Moses lifted up the serpent in the wilderness, even so must the Son of Man be lifted up;[15] so that whoever believes will in Him have eternal life.

[16] "For God so loved the world, that He gave His only begotten Son, that whoever believes in Him shall not perish, but have eternal life. [17] For God did not send the Son into the world to judge the world, but that the world might be saved through Him. [18] He who believes in Him is not judged; he who does not believe has been judged already, because he has not believed in the name of the only begotten Son of God. [19] This is the judgment, that the Light has come into the world, and men loved the darkness rather than the Light, for their deeds were evil.[20] For everyone who does evil hates the Light, and does not come to the Light for fear that his deeds will be exposed. [21] But he who practices the truth comes to the Light, so that his deeds may be manifested as having been wrought in God."

Thought Questions for Cheshvan 5782

When did Nicodemus come to Jesus? Why do you think he came at this time of day? Did you enter God's family through the Holy Spirit or are you trusting in works of the flesh like the Pharisees?

_____

_____

_____

_____

_____

Why do you think Nicodemus did not understand what Jesus meant? How do we gain understanding of spiritual things?

_____

_____

_____

_____

_____

Jesus told Nicodemus that he had to be born again. What did Jesus mean? What does this mean to you? How did Paul describe this new birth in 2 Corinthians 5:17?

_____

_____

_____

_____

_____

In this month of new beginnings - have you experienced this second birth? Jesus said, man enters through the door (natural birth - as He did), and later He says, "I AM the door" (spiritual birth) and anyone who enters through Him will be saved. Have you been born again?

_____

_____

_____

_____

_____

Who is a "Nicodemus" in your life?   What are some ways you can reach out and explain about the new birth in Christ?

_____

_____

_____

_____

_____

Cheshvan 5782

Yom Rishon (1st Day)	Yom Sheni (2nd Day)	Yom Sh'lishi (3rd Day)	Yom Revi'i (4th Day)
Sunday	Monday	Tuesday	Wednesday
			TISHREI 30 OCT 6 ○Rosh Chodesh CHESHVAN
4 OCT 10	5 OCT 11	6 OCT 12	7 OCT 13
11 OCT 17	12 OCT 18	13 OCT 19	14 ●OCT 20
18 OCT 24	19 OCT 25	20 OCT 26	21 OCT 27
25 OCT 31	26 NOV 1	27 NOV 2 ✿Noah Exited The Ark (A Year Later, Gen 8:14-20)	28 NOV 3

October/November 2021

Yom Chamishi (5th Day)	Yom Shishi (6th Day)	Yom Shabbat (The Shabbat)	Moed
Thursday	**Friday**	**Saturday**	**Season**
1 OCT 7 ○Rosh Chodesh CHESHVAN	2 OCT 8 🕯🕯 *Shabbat begins*	3 OCT 9 🕯 *Shabbat ends*	**Stav (Fall)** *Season of Repentance*
8 OCT 14	9 OCT 15 🕯🕯 *Shabbat begins*	10 OCT 16 ✡Noah Entered The Ark (Gen 7:1-5) 🕯 *Shabbat ends*	**Months of Stav** Tishrei *Month of Returning & Rejoicing* Cheshvan *New Beginnings* Kislev *Month of Hope*
15 OCT 21	16 OCT 22 🕯🕯 *Shabbat begins*	17 OCT 23 ✡The Flood Began (Gen 7:10-11) 🕯 *Shabbat ends*	**Tribes of Stav** Efrayim *Be Fruitful and Mulitiply* Menashe *He Made Me to Forget* Binyamiyn *Son of My Right Hand*
22 OCT 28	23 OCT 29 🕯🕯 *Shabbat begins*	24 OCT 30 🕯 *Shabbat ends*	**Notes**
29 NOV 4 ○Rosh Chodesh KISLEV			

Bible Portions for Cheshvan 5782

Read through the Torah in a year and glean from the Prophets and the New Testament.
Space provided for notes.

Week of:
Cheshvan 3, 5782/ Oct 9, 2021

Torah Portion: **Noach** *(Noah)* Gen 6:9- 11:32
Prophets Portion: Isa 54:1- 55:5
NT Portion: 1 Peter 3:18- 22

_____
_____
_____
_____
_____
_____

Week of:
Cheshvan 10, 5782/ Oct 16, 2021

Torah Portion: **Lecha Lecha** *(Go forth yourself)* Gen 12:1- 17:27
Prophets Portion: Isa 40:27- 41:16
NT Portion: Rom 4:1- 25

_____
_____
_____
_____
_____
_____

Week of:
Cheshvan 17, 5782/ Oct 23, 2021

Torah Portion: **Vayera** *(And He appeared)* Gen 18:1- 22:24
Prophets Portion: 2 Kings 4:1- 37
NT Portion: 2 Peter 2:4- 11

_____
_____
_____
_____
_____
_____

Week of:
Cheshvan 24, 5782/ Oct 30, 2021

Torah Portion: **Chavei Sarah** *(The life of Sarah)* Gen 23:1- 25:18
Prophets Portion: 1 Kings 1:1- 31
NT Portion: 1 Cor 15:30- 57

_____
_____
_____
_____
_____
_____

Kislev 5782

November 5 – December 4, 2021

Ninth Month of Spiritual Year
30 days

Confidence in The Dark in Kislev

Are you afraid of the dark? As I child I was afraid of the dark. I had to sleep with my bedroom door open and the hall light dimmed. I suppose it gave me some kind of comfort. The glow of the hallway light gave me the ability to rest. This is Kislev. The word Kislev means "trust, rest and security." This month, as the days grow shorter and the nights grow longer, the Lord reminds us He is our light in the darkness. When we draw near to Him, He draws near to us and we find His comfort. He illuminates our path so we can walk through this month in His confidence.

In Kislev, as the days grow darker, the Chanukah menorah shines brighter and brighter! Chanukah is known as the "Feast of Lights." Here's a little background on Chanukah. During the second temple period, the altar of the Lord was abandoned and soon desecrated by Antiochus Epiphanes, a Greek invader. The Maccabees were a strong priestly family of Israelites who refused to sit and watch the temple be defiled. They hammered the enemy and recaptured the temple for the Lord. In order to bring the temple back into use, the temple needed to be cleansed and rededicated. The word Chanukah means "dedication." Amongst the devastation of the temple, a small flask of sanctified oil was found. This amount was only enough to keep the lampstand illuminated for one day. Miraculously, the oil burned brightly for eight days. Hence, Chanukah is celebrated for eight days commemorating the miracle of the oil. What lesson is the Lord illuminating to us in Chanukah? He is reminding us not to abandon His altar. Let us stand firm in His ways. When we choose to stand, we become like a lampstand. As we allow the power of His Spirit to be released through us, His light illuminates the darkness. As we thank the Lord for what seems like "not enough", He will multiply it, providing hope and provision to us and loved ones along our path.

Kislev is also known as the "Month of Dreams." As the nights grow longer, we may find ourselves going to bed earlier. Let's be aware of our sleep patterns, especially our dreams. *"He gives to His beloved even in his sleep." (Ps 127:2)* We all dream and the Lord may speak to us in dreams. It could be one of warning or one of encouragement for our future. It's interesting to note the Torah portions for this month of Kislev have more dream references than any other time of the year. The portions in Kislev, Genesis 28 through Genesis 44, include dreamers like Jacob and Joseph. May we be aware of His communication to us when we rest our eyes. Let's ask Him to reveal any mysteries in our dreams as He did for Daniel (Dan 2:28) and commit to Him both, the dreams of our sleep and those of our heart.

Amidst the dark night sky of Kislev, the Lord shines brightly through the constellation Sagittarius. Sagittarius is a picture of the archer. The Lord underscores this trait in Benjamin, the tribe associated with this month, who were known as "Masters of The Art of The Bow." May the Lord teach us to shoot straight, move quickly and cut our losses. Benjamin was the beloved son born to Jacob and Rachel. Rachel took her last breath, immediately after giving birth to her son, and named him Ben-oni, "son of my pain." Jacob, however, quickly spoke a new name over him, calling him Benjamin, "son of my right hand" which was his true identity. Jesus in the flesh was a "man of sorrows." (Isa 53:3) But now He sits at the right hand of the Father in the Spirit. (Heb 10:12) As believers, we also sit with Him in heavenly places. Confidence arises when we renew our minds to our true identity in Christ. (Eph 2:6)

The Hebrew letter highlighted this month is the letter "Samech." Samech means "to lean upon or to support." It is reassuring to have someone to lean on when the days grow dark and obscure. Samech depicts coming full circle. Do you feel like you are coming full circle this month? Although this is the ninth month of the Hebrew calendar, it is the last month of the Gregorian calendar. He longs to be our support into 2022. Lean upon and trust in Him with your future, even if it appears uncertain to you in the natural. Be encouraged …for even the darkness is as light to Him! (Ps 139:12)

In this month of Kislev ask the Lord to identify anything you have been keeping in the dark. Allow His light to expose it and bring healing to you and others. Are there areas of your life where you have let your guard down? Use this time to regroup and focus, just as the Maccabees did. Be extra mindful of your sleeping patterns and ask the Lord to keep you alert to hear His voice, even in your day dreams and imaginations. May you glow through Kislev like the menorah of Chanukah, shining brighter and brighter every day with the miraculous Light of the world Himself, Yeshua! (Prov 4:18)

Journal for Kislev 5782

Use the space below to record your thoughts, praises and prayers for this month.

_____

_____

_____

_____

_____

_____

_____

_____

_____

_____

_____

_____

_____

_____

_____

_____

_____

_____

_____

_____

_____

_____

_____

_____

_____

_____

_____

_____

_____

_____

_____

_____

_____

_____

_____

_____

_____

Journal for Kislev 5782

Chalkboard Teaching for Kislev 5782

Go to "Chalkboard Teachings" page at www.christinevales.com or scan QR Code below.
Enjoy watching the chalkboard teaching for this month. Use space below to take notes.

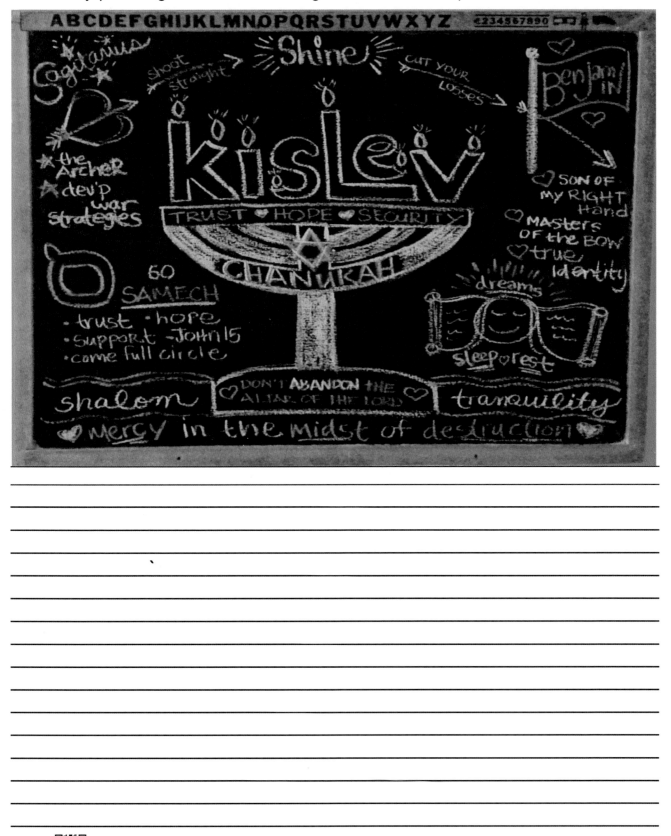

Scan QR code to go directly to "Chalkboard Teachings" page at www.christinevales.com.

128

Prophetic Fact Sheet for Kislev 5782

BABYLONIAN NAME
KISLEV •"Security", "Trust", "Restful Sleep"

HEBREW NAME
NONE

MONTH OF THE YEAR
9th MONTH OF SPIRITUAL YEAR
- •Hebrew Letter Tet = 9
- •A Choice of Life or Death:
  A Basket of Fruit, Womb, Fruit of Spirit (Gal 5) **OR**
  A Basket w/Twisted Snake, Finality, Judgment, To Surround

3rd MONTH OF PHYSICAL/CIVIL YEAR
- •Hebrew Letter Gimel = 3
- •A Camel, Provision, Lifted Up, Divine Fullness, Trinity

SEASON (Moed)
STAV (Fall) •Season of Repentance

TRIBES of STAV •Efrayim, Menashe, Binyamiyn

MONTHLY THEMES of STAV
TISHREI	•Month of Returning & Rejoicing
CHESHVAN	•New Beginnings
KISLEV	•Month of Hope

APPOINTED TIMES (Moedim)
KISLEV 1	✿**ROSH CHODESH KISLEV** (Head of Month, Kislev)
	•Ps 81:1-4
KISLEV 24-	✿**CHANUKAH** (Feast of Dedication)
TEVET 2	•Jn 10:22

✿**Something to Note…** Many Biblical scholars believe that Messiah was born in Tishrei, during Succot. Yeshua may have possibly been conceived in this month of Kislev. If so, consider Yeshua, The Light of the world, may have been conceived during the darkest time of the year. Consider even still, He may have been conceived on the darkest day of the year. Something to ponder…

COLORS/GEMSTONES
COLORS	Multicolor, Rainbow
GEMSTONES	Opal, Jasper

TRIBE OF ISRAEL
BINYAMIYN (Benjamin)
- •"Son of My Right Hand"
- •12th Son of Ya'akov (Jacob)
- •2nd Son by Rachel (Gen 35:16-18)

Ya'akov's Prophetic Blessing (Gen 49:27) *"Binyamiyn is a ravenous wolf. In the morning he devours the prey and in the evening he divides the spoil."*
- •Camped west of tabernacle w/Efrayim & Menashe (Num 2)
- •Flag: Multi-color with a wolf on it (Gen 49:27)
- •Only child born in the Promised Land
- •The Archer, The Master of The Art of the Bow
- •Many left-handed warriors (Judg 20:16)

HEBREW LETTER

SAMEKH
- •15th Letter of the Hebrew Alphabet
- •Numerical Value 60
- •Priestly Blessing
- •Number of letters in Aaronic Blessing (Num 6:23-27)
- •To Trust, Support, Come Full Circle
- •To Lean Upon, Uphold, Prop (Jn 15)
- •A Slow Twisting of Turning Aside
- •The Lord's encompassing support

ACTION/BODY PART
SLEEPING	•He gives to His beloved even in his sleep (Ps 127:2)
STOMACH	

CONSTELLATION
KESITH (Sagittarius)
- •The Archer
- •Shoot straight, move quickly, cut your losses and move on
- •Pull bow back w/ Right Arm of The Lord, Yeshua (Isa 53:1)
- •Put on full armor of God (Eph 6)
- •Time to stand against empires & cultures (Eph 6:12)
- •Stand against the enemy & he will flee (Eph 6:10-18, Jas 4:7)

MONTHLY CHARACTERISTICS
- •Month of hope, rest and trust
- •Enter His rest knowing you are His beloved (1 Jn 4:18, Heb 4)
- •Tap into His supernatural peace within you (Gal 5:22-23)
- •Month of dreams/Bring dreams before the Lord (Ps 127:2)
- •Note sleeping patterns
- •Torah portions of Kislev are full of dreams (Gen 28:10-44:17)
- •Shortest (darkest) day of the year falls in this month
- •Shine as lights in the world (Phil 2:12-16)
- •Our joy is our light (Prov 13:9)
- •Chanukah begins (only appointed time in two months)
- •Stand fast like the Maccabees (Phil 4:1, Zech 4:6)
- •Don't abandon the altar of The Lord
- •Mediate on the vine & the branches (Jn 15)
- •His mercies reign in the midst of destruction
- •Keep eye on Israel (Ps 122:6)

Kislev 5782
Bible Study & Thought Questions
For Individual & Group Study

Dive into this portion of the New Testament for further reflection on the theme of the month. Ponder thought questions that follow and use space for personal reflection and group study.

Matthew 25:1-13

"Then the kingdom of heaven will be comparable to ten virgins, who took their lamps and went out to meet the bridegroom. [2] Five of them were foolish, and five were prudent. [3] For when the foolish took their lamps, they took no oil with them, [4] but the prudent took oil in flasks along with their lamps. [5] Now while the bridegroom was delaying, they all got drowsy and began to sleep. [6] But at midnight there was a shout, 'Behold, the bridegroom! Come out to meet him.' [7] Then all those virgins rose and trimmed their lamps. [8] The foolish said to the prudent, 'Give us some of your oil, for our lamps are going out.' [9] But the prudent answered, 'No, there will not be enough for us and you too; go instead to the dealers and buy some for yourselves.' [10] And while they were going away to make the purchase, the bridegroom came, and those who were ready went in with him to the wedding feast; and the door was shut. [11] Later the other virgins also came, saying, 'Lord, lord, open up for us.' [12] But he answered, 'Truly I say to you, I do not know you.' [13] Be on the alert then, for you do not know the day nor the hour.

Thought Questions for Kislev 5782

Who do you think these young virgins in Matthew 25 represent? How many virgins had oil in their lamps?

_____
_____
_____
_____
_____
_____

Why didn't the prudent virgins give some of their oil to the foolish virgins?

_____
_____
_____
_____
_____
_____

How is this parable comparable to the kingdom of heaven? What does the oil represent?

_____
_____
_____
_____
_____
_____

How do you get "oil" in your lamp and more in your flasks? What will be the reward for being prepared for His return?

_____
_____
_____
_____
_____

This month, the Lord reminds us to stand and shine! Describe the steps you are taking to be a light in this world.

_____
_____
_____
_____
_____

Kislev 5782

Yom Rishon (1st Day)	Yom Sheni (2nd Day)	Yom Sh'lishi (3rd Day)	Yom Revi'i (4th Day)
Sunday	**Monday**	**Tuesday**	**Wednesday**
3 NOV 7	4 NOV 8	5 NOV 9	6 NOV 10
10 NOV 14	11 NOV 15	12 NOV 16	13 NOV 17
17 NOV 21	18 NOV 22	19 NOV 23	20 NOV 24
24 NOV 28 ✡Chanukah (Feast of Dedication, Day 1)	25 NOV 29 ✡Chanukah (Feast of Dedication, Day 2)	26 NOV 30 ✡Chanukah (Feast of Dedication, Day 3)	27 DEC 1 ✡Chanukah (Feast of Dedication, Day 4)

November/December 2021

Yom Chamishi (5th Day)	Yom Shishi (6th Day)	Yom Shabbat (The Shabbat)	Moed
Thursday	**Friday**	**Saturday**	Season
CHESHVAN 29 NOV 4 ◗Rosh Chodesh KISLEV	1 NOV 5 ◗Rosh Chodesh KISLEV 🕯🕯Shabbat begins	2 NOV 6 🕯 Shabbat ends	**Stav (Fall)** *Season of Repentance*
7 NOV 11	8 NOV 12 🕯🕯 Shabbat begins	9 NOV 13 🕯 Shabbat ends	**Months of Stav** Tishrei *Month of Returning & Rejoicing* Cheshvan *New Beginnings* Kislev *Month of Hope*
14 NOV 18	15 ●NOV 19 🕯🕯 Shabbat begins	16 NOV 20 🕯 Shabbat ends	**Tribes of Stav** Efrayim *Be Fruitful and Mulitiply* Menashe *He Made Me to Forget* Binyamiyn *Son of My Right Hand*
21 NOV 25 🕎Thanksgiving (US National Day of Thanks & Harvest)	22 NOV 26 🕯🕯 Shabbat begins	23 NOV 27 🕯 Shabbat ends	**Notes**
28 DEC 2 ✡Chanukah 🕯🕯🕯🕯🕯 (Feast of Dedication, Day 5)	29 DEC 3 ✡Chanukah 🕯🕯🕯🕯🕯🕯 (Feast of Dedication, Day 6) 🕯🕯 Shabbat begins	30 DEC 4 ✡Chanukah 🕯🕯🕯🕯🕯🕯🕯 (Feast of Dedication, Day 7) ◗Rosh Chodesh TEVET 🕯 Shabbat ends	

Bible Portions for Kislev 5782

Read through the Torah in a year and glean from the Prophets and the New Testament.
Space provided for notes.

Week of:
Kislev 2, 5782/ Nov 6, 2021

Torah Portion: **Toldot** *(Generations)* Gen 25:19- 28:9
Prophets Portion: Mal 1:1- 2:7
NT Portion: Rom 9:6- 13

_____
_____
_____
_____

Week of:
Kislev 9, 5782/ Nov 13, 2021

Torah Portion: **Vayetze** *(And he went out)* Gen 28:10- 32:2
Prophets Portion: Hos 12:13- 14:9
NT Portion: John 1:43- 51

_____
_____
_____
_____

Week of:
Kislev 16, 5782/ Nov 20, 2021

Torah Portion: **Vayishlach** *(And he sent)* Gen 32:3- 36:43
Prophets Portion: Obad 1:1- 21
NT Portion: Matt 26:36- 46

_____
_____
_____
_____

Week of:
Kislev 23, 5782/ Nov 27, 2021

Torah Portion: **Vayeshev** *(And he settled)* Gen 37:1- 40:23
Prophets Portion: Amos 2:6- 3:8
NT Portion: Acts 7:9- 16

_____
_____
_____
_____

Week of:
Kislev 30, 5782/ Dec 4, 2021

Torah Portion: **Miketz** *(At the end of)* Gen 41:1- 44:17
Prophets Portion: 1 Kings 3:15- 4:1
NT Portion: 1 Cor 2:1- 5

_____
_____
_____
_____

Tevet 5782

December 5, 2021 – January 2, 2022

Tenth Month of Spiritual Year
29 days

It's Tevet... How Old Are You Now?

Remember Tevet? We have been around this month before and as you may recall, this month is about growing up. This has nothing to do with age, but with maturity. Before we break out the cake and candles, lets take another look at Tevet and see how far we've come. For a quick refresher on Tevet, flip back and review last year's monthly narrative and journal notes. After you review, let's meet back here.

Each time we travel through a month, it is always good to look back to see where we came from and what we learned. The word Tevet means "good." Growing up may be hard but is necessary and truly a "good" thing. So, how are we progressing? Our life and actions are a testimony revealing our maturity and growth. How is our perspective? Have we learned to look at things with our "good eye?" Are we still reasoning as a child or have we grown into a man or woman of God? (1 Cor 13:11) Is our talk seasoned with salt or self? Do the things that upset us last year, still stir us up this year? (Eph 4:26) Are we as easily offended or are we applying His good sense to overlook an offense? (Prov 19:11) We will always have areas where we need to mature, but checking our progress with Him is truly wisdom in itself. It is His will for us to move from grace to grace and glory to glory.

As we learned last year, signs of maturity are displayed in how we control our emotions and passions. One area of passion most of us have is eating. Talk about growing! Refraining ourselves from food can help us grow real fast... literally! Fasting, like any form of discipline, doesn't seem fun at the time but the physical and spiritual benefits truly are beneficial. Tevet is connected with our liver, which filters our blood. Fasting expedites and enhances the cleansing process. In addition to purifying our blood and body, fasting also brings clarity in our thoughts and prayers. If there was ever a perfect time for a fast, Tevet is it! Think about it, not only is it wise to fast after all the holiday eats and treats, but this is highlighted in the month of Tevet. The 10th of Tevet is a minor fast, commemorating the beginning of the siege of Jerusalem by Nebuchadnezzar. This siege led Israel into captivity for seventy years and brought the destruction of the first temple. (2 Kings 25:1-2)

Another "fast" way we grow is when we face persecution. During these times, the Lord calls us to grow up and rise up in our identity in Him. He reminds us He has overcome the world and has also given us power and authority over the enemy. (Lk 10:19) He commands us to be bold and courageous. (Jos 1:7) If we come up short, He encourages us by His word reminding us of our true identity and position of victory in Him. His word transforms us from young cubs into bold lions in the Spirit. Now that's knowing... "if God is for us, who can be against us?" (Rom 8:31)

Lastly, let us not allow fear to take a foothold in our lives. Are we still afraid of the same things we were last year or have we overcome? Let's be sure to celebrate those areas of our lives where He has given us courage and victory! The Lord knows how susceptible we are to fear. The Bible instructs us to "fear not" three hundred and sixty-five times. It's as if the Lord is reminding us to receive and focus on His great love for us every day. When we fall into fear, it's an indicator we have not had a revelation of God's love in that area of our life. Fear and anxiety take over when we forget to factor God and His love for us into the equation of our situation. When we magnify Him and His love for us, our problems become smaller and our knowledge of Him and His love for us grows larger. Our fears subside, and our faith arises. As His Word promises, *"There is no fear in love. But perfect love casts out fear."* (1 Jn 4:18) and *"Faith works by love."* (Gal 5:6) Knowing we're loved, causes us to walk in His confidence even as we enter into the new Gregorian calendar year. Let's be reminded of this truth moving forward with Him... *"The Lord himself goes before you and will be with you. He will never leave you nor forsake you. Do not be afraid."* (Deut 31:8)

So, how old are you now? Take some time to access your maturity from last year and praise Him for the victories regardless of age. What are those areas where you still need to grow? Do you feel led to fast this month? Are you facing persecution? Be reminded of your authority in Christ and rise up in the boldness of His Spirit. Is fear is rearing it's ugly head? Ask the Lord to show you how much He loves you and watch His perfect love cast out fear in your heart. As you move forward, be sure of this... He who began a good work in you will be faithful to complete it and will not abandon the work of His hands. (Phil 1:6, Ps 138:8)

Journal for Tevet 5782

Use the space below to record your thoughts, praises and prayers for this month.

_____
_____
_____
_____
_____
_____
_____
_____
_____
_____
_____
_____
_____
_____
_____
_____
_____
_____
_____
_____
_____
_____
_____
_____
_____
_____
_____
_____
_____
_____
_____
_____
_____
_____
_____
_____

Go to "Chalkboard Teachings" page at www.christinevales.com or scan QR Code below.
Enjoy watching the chalkboard teaching for this month. Use space below to take notes.

 Scan QR code to go directly to "Chalkboard Teachings" page at www.christinevales.com.

138

Prophetic Fact Sheet for Tevet 5782

BABYLONIAN NAME
TEVET
- "Good", "Divine Grace"
- From Hebrew "Tov" = Good

HEBREW NAME
NONE

MONTH OF THE YEAR
10th MONTH OF SPIRITUAL YEAR
- Hebrew Letter Yod = 10
- A Closed Hand, Appointed Mercy from The Hand of God
- An Action, Work, Humility, Holiness, Godly Authority
- Number of Order, Tithe, Testimony

4th MONTH OF PHYSICAL/CIVIL YEAR
- Hebrew Letter Dalet = 4
- A Door, Path, The Way of Life, Creativity

SEASON (Moed)
HOREF (Winter) •Season of Victory & Joy

TRIBES of HOREF •Dan, Asher, Naftali

THEMES of HOREF
TEVET	•Maturing in Him
SH'VAT	•His Righteousness is My Foundation
ADAR	•His Joy is My Strength

APPOINTED TIMES (Moedim)
TEVET 1	**ROSH CHODESH TEVET** (Head of Month, Tevet) •Ps 81:1-4
KISLEV 24- TEVET 2	**CHANUKAH** (Feast of Dedication) •Jn 10:22
TEVET 10	**ASARAH B'TEVET** (Tevet 10) •Minor Fast Day •Nebuchadnezzar's siege of Jerusalem 587 BC •2 Kings 25:1-2, Eze 33:21, Zech 8:19

COLORS/GEMSTONES
COLORS	Dark Blue, Turquoise
GEMSTONES	Sapphire, Turquoise

TRIBE OF ISRAEL
DAN
- "To Rule", "Judge", "Grow Up", "Mature"
- 5th Son of Ya'akov (Jacob)
- 1st Son by Rachel's Maid, Bilhah (Gen 30:4-6)

Ya'akov's Prophetic Blessing (Gen 49:16-18) *"Dan shall judge his people, as one of the tribes of Yisra'el. Dan shall be a serpent in the way, a horned snake in the path that bites the horse's heels, so that his rider falls backward. For Your salvation I wait, O LORD."*
- Camped north of tabernacle w/Asher & Naftali (Num 2)
- Flag: Black and white with a serpent (Gen 49:17)
- Could take down the enemy w/o touching them (Jdg 16)

HEBREW LETTER

AYIN
- 16th Letter of the Hebrew Alphabet
- Numerical Value 70
- Perfection, Spiritual Order
- An Eye, Spring, Well
- To Watch, Know, Understand, Obey, Focus On

ACTION/BODY PART
ANGER	•Be angry but sin not (Gal 5, Eph 4:26)
LIVER	•Fasting purifies the blood

CONSTELLATION
GEDI (Capricorn)
- The Goat, The Cut Off, Offering
- Goat was sin offering for Israel (Lev 10:16-17)
- Jesus our Scapegoat/Perfect Atoning Sacrifice (Heb 9-10)

MONTHLY CHARACTERISTICS
- Month of growing up (1 Cor 13:11, Heb 12:11)
- Follow His lead on the path to your destiny (Prov 4:18)
- Month to get focused (Hab 2:2)
- Time to get priorities in order (Prv 16:3,9)
- Let His Word to be a lamp onto your feet (Ps 119:105)
- Declare His promises over your life (Ps 119:49)
- Review prophetic words (Deut 28:1-14, 2Cor 1:20)
- Review education for your next phase of life (Prv 1-4)
- Keep your eyes fixed on Jesus (2 Cor 4:18, Heb 12:2)
- See w/ your good eye/ War against evil eye (Matt 6:22-23)
- Evaluate from your seat in heavenly places (Eph 2:6)
- His eyes seek to support those whose heart is His (2 Chron 16:9)
- "Holy anger"/ Be angry but sin not (Gal 5, Eph 4:26)
- Stand for your inheritance (Dan 12:13)
- Leap out of fear and passivity (2 Tim 1:7)
- Put on your armor and stand (Eph 6:10-18, Jas 4:7)
- Pray for new artistic expressions in worship
- Pray for your commander in chief and authority figures
- Consider fasting/ Brings body into order (Matt 4:4)
- Capitalize on downtime to study His Word (2 Tim 2:15)
- Gregorian year ends

Tevet 5782
Bible Study & Thought Questions
For Individual & Group Study

Dive into this portion of the New Testament for further reflection on the theme of the month. Ponder thought questions that follow and use space for personal reflection and group study.

1 Corinthians 3:1-9

And I, brethren, could not speak to you as to spiritual men, but as to men of flesh, as to infants in Christ. [2] I gave you milk to drink, not solid food; for you were not yet able to receive it. Indeed, even now you are not yet able, [3] for you are still fleshly. For since there is jealousy and strife among you, are you not fleshly, and are you not walking like mere men? [4] For when one says, "I am of Paul," and another, "I am of Apollos," are you not mere men? [5] What then is Apollos? And what is Paul? Servants through whom you believed, even as the Lord gave opportunity to each one. [6] I planted, Apollos watered, but God was causing the growth. [7] So then neither the one who plants nor the one who waters is anything, but God who causes the growth. [8] Now he who plants and he who waters are one; but each will receive his own reward according to his own labor. [9] For we are God's fellow workers; you are God's field, God's building.

Hebrews 5:11-14

[11] Concerning him we have much to say, and it is hard to explain, since you have become dull of hearing. [12] For though by this time you ought to be teachers, you have need again for someone to teach you the elementary principles of the oracles of God, and you have come to need milk and not solid food. [13] For everyone who partakes only of milk is not accustomed to the word of righteousness, for he is an infant. [14] But solid food is for the mature, who because of practice have their senses trained to discern good and evil.

Thought Questions for Tevet 5782

Who was Paul speaking to and why did he want them to experience "solid food?"

_____
_____
_____
_____
_____
_____

What part did Paul have in sharing with his Corinthian brothers? What part did Apollos play?
What part did God play?

_____
_____
_____
_____
_____
_____

Why was Paul unable to speak to them as spiritual men?

_____
_____
_____
_____
_____
_____

Have you transitioned from milk to meat? If yes- what results have you seen? If no- what steps are
you taking to "having your senses trained to discern good and evil?" (Heb 5:14)

_____
_____
_____
_____
_____

As you have made it to the month of "growing up" again- what areas of your life have you grown in
maturity? How did this growth occur?

_____
_____
_____
_____
_____

Tevet 5782

Sunday	Monday	Tuesday	Wednesday
Yom Rishon (1st Day)	Yom Sheni (2nd Day)	Yom Sh'lishi (3rd Day)	Yom Revi'i (4th Day)
1 DEC 5 ○Rosh Chodesh TEVET ✡Chanukah 🕎 (Feast of Dedication, Day 8)	**2** DEC 6 ✡Chanukah Ends (Feast of Dedication)	**3** DEC 7	**4** DEC 8
8 DEC 12	**9** DEC 13	**10** DEC 14 ✡Asarah B'Tevet (10th of Tevet)	**11** DEC 15
15 DEC 19	**16** DEC 20	**17** DEC 21	**18** DEC 22
22 DEC 26 **29** JAN 2 ○Rosh Chodesh SH'VAT	**23** DEC 27	**24** DEC 28	**25** DEC 29

December 2021/January 2022

Thursday	Friday	Saturday	Moed
Yom Chamishi (5th Day)	**Yom Shishi** (6th Day)	**Yom Shabbat** (The Shabbat)	**Season**
		KISLEV 30 DEC 4 ✡Chanukah (Feast of Dedication, Day 7) ○Rosh Chodesh TEVET *Shabbat ends*	**Horaf (Winter)** *Season of Victory & Joy*
5 DEC 9	**6** DEC 10 *Shabbat begins*	**7** DEC 11 *Shabbat ends*	**Months of Horaf** Tevet *Maturing in Him* Sh'vat *His Righteousness is My Foundation* Adar *His Joy is My Strength*
12 DEC 16	**13** DEC 17 *Shabbat begins*	**14** ●DEC 18 *Shabbat ends*	**Tribes of Horaf** Dan *To Rule, To Judge, To Mature* Asher *Pleasure, Happinesss, Delicious* Naftali *Sweetness to me*
19 DEC 23	**20** DEC 24 *Shabbat begins*	**21** DEC 25 ✝Christmas (Christian Date Celebrating Yeshua's Birth) *Shabbat ends*	**Notes**
26 DEC 30	**27** DEC 31 *Shabbat begins*	**28** JAN 1 ⌂New Year's Day 2022 (New Year Begins on Gregorian Calendar) *Shabbat ends*	

Bible Portions for Tevet 5782

Read through the Torah in a year and glean from the Prophets and the New Testament.
Space provided for notes.

Week of:
Tevet 7, 5782/ Dec 11, 2021

Torah Portion: **Vayigash** *(And he drew near)* Gen 44:18- 47:27
Prophets Portion: Eze 37:15- 28
NT Portion: Luke 6:9- 16

_____
_____
_____
_____
_____
_____
_____

Week of:
Tevet 14, 5782/ Dec 18, 2021

Torah Portion: **Vayechi** *(And he lived)* Gen 47:28- 50:26
Prophets Portion: 1 Kings 2:1- 12
NT Portion: 1 Pet 1:3- 9

_____
_____
_____
_____
_____
_____
_____

Week of:
Tevet 21, 5782/ Dec 25, 2021

Torah Portion: **Shemot** *(Names)* Exo 1:1- 6:1
Prophets Portion: Isa 27:6- 28:13, 29:22- 23
NT Portion: Acts 7:17- 29

_____
_____
_____
_____
_____
_____
_____

Week of:
Tevet 28, 5782/ Jan 1, 2022

Torah Portion: **Va'era** *(And I appeared)* Exo 6:2- 9:35
Prophets Portion: Eze 28:25- 29:21
NT Portion: Rom 9:14- 24

_____
_____
_____
_____
_____
_____
_____

Reflections & Resources

"There is an appointed time for everything.
And there is a time for every event under heaven."
Ecclesiastes 3:1

Year In Review

Look back and record highlights, scriptures and revelations month by month in the space below.

Tevet 5781

_____
_____
_____

Sh'vat 5781

_____
_____
_____

Adar 5781

_____
_____
_____

Nissan 5781

_____
_____
_____

Iyar 5781

_____
_____
_____

Sivan 5781

_____
_____
_____

Tammuz 5781

_____
_____
_____

Year In Review

Look back and record highlights, revelations and significant events month by month in space below.

Av 5781

_____
_____
_____

Elul 5781

_____
_____
_____

Year 5781

_____
_____
_____

Tishrei 5782

_____
_____
_____

Cheshvan 5782

_____
_____
_____

Kislev 5782

_____
_____
_____

Tevet 5782

_____
_____
_____

Notes

Notes

References Used

Books

"The Bible"
Adonai

"A Time To Advance"
Chuck Pierce, Robert and Linda Heidler

"A Time To Prosper"
Chuck Pierce and Robert Heidler

"God's Day Timer"
Mark Biltz

"How to Find, Follow, Fulfill God's Will"
Andrew Wommack

"The Book of Mysteries"
Jonathan Cahn

"The Feasts of the Lord"
Kevin Howard and Marvin Rosenthal

"The Messianic Church Arising"
Robert Heidler

"The Secret Hidden In Plain Sight'
Hoppy Bishop

"The Witness of The Stars"
EW Bullinger

Ministries

Andrew Wommack Ministries
Andrew Wommack
www.awmi.net

El Shaddai Ministries
Mark Biltz
www.elshaddaiministries.us

Galilee Calendar Company
Torah Portions
www.galileecalendarcompany.com

Glory of Zion International Ministries
Chuck Pierce and Robert Heidler
www.gloryofzion.org

Hebcal
Hebrew Calendar
www.hebcal.org

Hebrew For Christians
John Parsons
www.hebrew4christians.com

Hope of The World
Jonathan Cahn
www.hopeoftheworld.org

Zola Levitt Ministries
www.levitt.com

For Further Study

Books

"The Bible"
Adonai

"Handfuls of Purpose"
Bill Yount

"Hearing God"
Barry Bennett

"Spirit, Soul & Body"
Andrew Wommack

"The Believer's Authority"
Andrew Wommack

"The Complete Works of Josephus"
Flavius Josephus

"The Genesis Record"
Henry M. Morris

"The Power of Imagination"
Andrew Wommack

"Unlock Your Inheritance"
Susan Cheatham

Ministries

Andrew Wommack Ministries
www.awmi.net

Blowing The Shofar Ministries
www.billyount.com

El Shaddai Ministries
www.elshaddaiministries.us

Glory of Zion International Ministries
www.gloryofzion.org

Hebcal/Hebrew Calendar
www.hebcal.org

Hebrew For Christians
www.hebrew4christians.com

Hope of The World
www.hopeoftheworld.org

House of Peace/Beth Shalom
www.mylesandkatharineweiss.org

Jewish Voice
www.jewishvoice.org

One In Messiah Ministries
www.oimm.org

Reliant Family Church
www.reliantfamilychurch.com

Susan Cheatham Ministries
www.scmfire.org

Made in the USA
Columbia, SC
05 November 2020

23955353R10091